BARRIER ISLAND HANDBOOK

Dr. Stephen P. Leatherman

The University of Maryland

Coastal Publications Series
Laboratory for Coastal Research
The University of Maryland
College Park, Maryland 20742

1988

D1208443

Third Edition, 1988
Second Edition, 1982
First Edition, 1979

Contents

Acknowledgements

This Handbook was originally made possible by support from the National Park Service. Mr. Michael Mow drafted a number of the original figures, and Ms. Sue Gibbons was the illustrator for the Second Edition. The graphics for this edition were completed by Ms. Guinn Cooper, and Professor Joe Wiedel consulted in the cartographic design.

The cover is a Landsat satellite image of the Cape Lookout area, North Carolina, courtesy of the National Aeronautics and Space Administration (NASA). Vegetation appears red in this infrared (false) color scene, acquired on March 23, 1976.

Introduction

Origin of Islands

Barrier Types

Coastal barriers stretch in an irregular chain from Maine to Texas (Figure 1). These elongated, narrow landforms are composed of sand and other loose sediments transported by waves, currents, and wind. The term "barrier" identifies the structure as one that protects other features, such as lagoons and salt marshes, from direct wave attack of the open ocean.

Barriers are dynamic landforms; this often leads to conflict with human development. The shoreline is in constant flux, eroding or accreting in concert with changing energy conditions. This dynamic character contrasts with static structures such as houses and roads. These landforms also tend to be quite low (5 to 10 feet); in fact, over 90 percent of the barriers along the U.S. coastline are subject to flooding during major storms. In spite of the natural hazards, barrier development has burgeoned during the last few decades, particularly along the U.S. East coast which has coincidentally experienced a storm lull; the last major hurricane to hit was Donna in 1960.

Due to intense development pressures on coastal barriers, there has been a recent surge in research to determine their geologic and geomorphic characteristics in order to define more clearly barrier dynamics and susceptibility to storm damage. Along the northern New England coast and the Georgia bight, where tidal ranges are large (6 to 12 feet, mesotidal; Figure 1), barriers tend to be more stable than their microtidal (< 6 feet) counterparts. Since the preponderance of U.S. East and Gulf coast barriers are elongated, low, storm-vulnerable (microtidal) features, this Handbook was primarily written to describe them and the associated problems for human habitation.

State	Number of Islands	Total Acreage	Barrier Length (miles)
Alabama	5	28,200	59
Connecticut	14	2,362	21
Delaware	2	10,100	49
Florida	80	467,710	731
Georgia	15	165,600	105
Louisiana	18	41,120	147
Maine	9	2,640	28
Maryland	2	14,300	31
Massachusetts	27	37,600	216
Mississippi	5	9,500	37
New Hampshire	2	1,100	8
New Jersey	10	48,000	106
New York	15	30,310	173
North Carolina	23	146,400	324
Rhode Island	6	3,660	37
South Carolina	35	144,150	153
Texas	16	383,500	350
Virginia	11	68,900	111
18 States	295	1,605,152	2,686

1. Representative coastal barriers of the U.S. East and Gulf coasts.

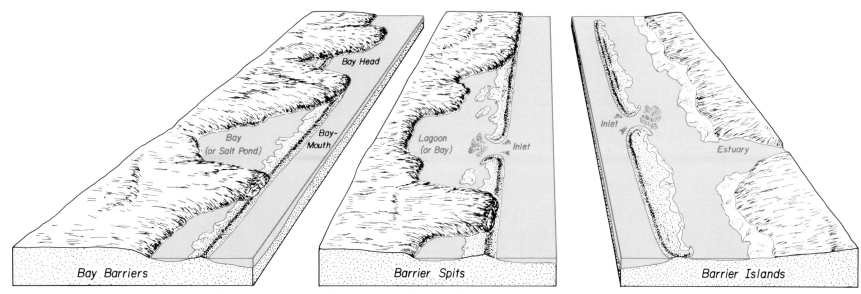

2.   Types of coastal barriers: Bay Barriers, Barrier Spits, and Barrier Islands.

Major types of coastal barriers are shown in Figure 2. Barrier islands, the most common such landform, are bounded on each side by inlets. Bay barriers, by contrast, are connected to headlands on both ends. They are largely restricted to the New England coast. Barrier spits are attached to a source of sediment but can be converted into islands by inlet severance of this connection. In many cases a small barrier spit can develop on the flanks of a barrier island.

The fact that barrier systems enclose estuaries and lagoons, which serve as the nursery ground for numerous marine species, makes these landforms especially important in maintaining the productivity of the coastal zone. Barrier changes, either natural or artificially induced, can affect estuarine system performance. These closely related systems have evolved together and can withstand the dynamic nature of the oceanic environment, but are susceptible to human disturbance.

Barrier islands can originate and develop in a number of different ways. There are three main theories of barrier island genesis: (1) spit growth and later segmentation by inlets; (2) mainland beach ridge submergence; and (3) upbuilding of submarine bars.

Along the U.S. northeast coast of the United States (from New York northward -- the region directly affected by the last Ice Age), spit accretion by littoral drift appears to be the characteristic manner in which barrier islands have formed. Barrier systems form as sand is transported from a source, such as sea cliffs and associated beaches, toward a region of accretion and sedimentation in open water (Figure 3). The result is a spit -- an elongate, fingerlike ridge composed of beach sediment that is attached at one end to the mainland but terminates in open water. Some barriers clearly grew laterally as long spits and were converted into barrier islands with inlet truncation (Figure 3). The Province Lands, Nauset Spit, and Monomoy Island on Cape Cod, Massachusetts, all originated by this process. The barrier island system along the south shore of Long Island, New York, probably developed in this manner.

The mechanism for barrier island formation along the U.S. southeast Atlantic and Gulf coasts is somewhat more complex and controversial. Hoyt proposed that as sea level rose, dune ridges on the seaward edge of the mainland were converted to barrier islands. The lower areas behind these ridges were flooded, creating lagoons (Figure 4).

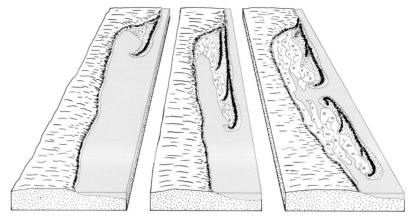

3. Barrier island formation by spit accretion and inlet breaching.

This could explain the development of the Outer Banks of North Carolina. Conversely, the Carolina capes may have evolved from Pleistocene-age river deltas formed when sea level was 300 feet lower than present (see Figure 50). As sea level rose during the past 15,000 years, these large deltaic sand bodies were reworked by waves and currents and pushed landward. In the process, sand spits could have grown off these eroding deltaic headlands, forming the barriers that eventually bridged the capes.

The third possible mechanism for barrier island formation is by submarine bar upbuilding. Material from the nearshore bottom is transported by waves and currents to form an offshore bar (or shoal) that could eventually build above sea level as an emergent barrier. Comparison of historical aerial photographs and charts has shown that some small Gulf coast islands have originated by this means. However, a major barrier island chain could not develop from emerging shoals since sedi-

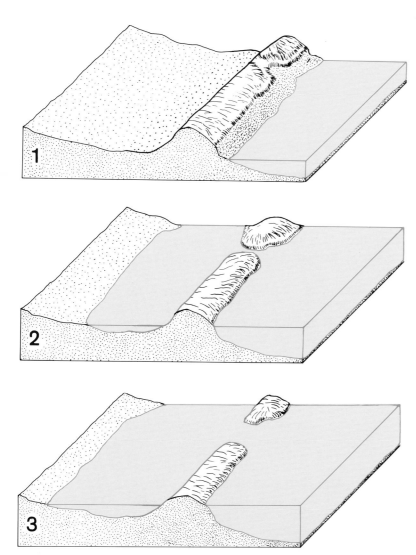

4. Hoyt's theory of barrier island formation by drowning of a mainland dune ridge.

ment supplies are insufficient and wave energy is too high in most coastal areas.

Coastal barriers may also form at the mouths of major rivers which deposit large quantities of sediment into the ocean. For instance, sandy barriers have developed on the Mississippi River delta through wave erosion and reworking of these riverine sediments. By contrast, small barriers can develop where rivers empty into the sea without forming large deltas. Popham Beach and Reid State Park along the southeastern Maine coast formed as bay barriers in this manner.

Marshy platforms or cheniers can originate in a low-energy environment, where a large proportion of the sediment in transport is silt, clay and very fine sand. Ridges are created when storm surges push sandy/shelly sediment landward from the shore for deposition on the marsh surface. These strandplains, which are not true barriers, are best developed along the western Louisiana-Mississippi coastline (see Figure 19).

Modern (Holocene) barrier islands can also be welded onto older coastal plain remnants, which were cut off from the mainland by sea level rise to become isolated as islands (see Figure 18). Thus the core of these sea islands consists of higher elevation Pleistocene sediments, which were deposited prior to the last Ice Age. Cumberland and Sapelo Islands, Georgia, are good examples of this type of landform.

Barriers have been reshaped by waves and currents over geologic time since their initial formation. Although an island may have developed by any of the above mechanisms, subsequent changes due to landward migration have resulted in major alterations to its original geomorphic structure. The type of barrier island found in a given geographical region reflects the geological history, sediment supply, energy conditions, and relative sea level changes unique to that area.

Barrier Types

There are essentially two ways to examine barrier island morphology -- topographic form and geomorphic expression. Topography reflects the influence of storm-induced overwash and inlet processes relative to dune building processes. Barrier topography can be affected greatly by human intervention, such as dune stabilization programs. Also, previous misuses of the land, such as woodcutting and overgrazing, have resulted in large-scale devegetation and dune migration.

Barriers vary considerably with regard to their overall geomorphic expression. Coastal barriers are initially classified as bay barriers, barrier spits and barrier islands (Figure 2). This first separation is dependent upon the nature of attachment of the barrier to the mainland, if at all. Subsequent barrier class divisions are made according to barrier shape.

Bay Barriers

Coastal barriers that are connected at both ends to headlands are called bay barriers. These barriers are typically small and common along highly indented coastlines, where rock or glacially-formed headlands jut into the sea. Bay barriers usually do not have permanent inlets, but temporary openings occasionally occur.

Bayhead barriers are found in the upper reaches of a bay and form where the outer coastal cliffs are resistant to erosion (Figure 5). While some sandy sediments may be supplied from sea cliff

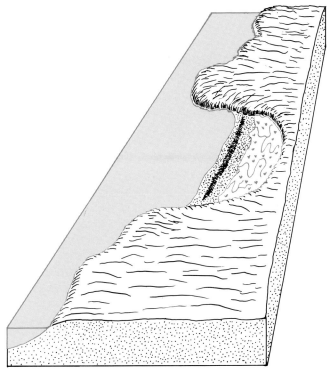

5.   Bayhead Barrier.

erosion, much of the material necessary to form the
barrier feature is derived from other sources, such
as sand from adjacent rivers and occasionally from
shell debris accumulation.   Bayhead barriers are
common in northern New England, where crystalline
granite rocks form an irregular coastline.   Sand
Beach in Acadia National Park, Maine, is a classic
example of a bayhead barrier.   Most of the sand
composing this small barrier is derived from shells
of marine animals that are ground to sand-size
particles by wave action.

Coastal barriers that connect headlands along

the outer reaches of an embayment are called
baymouth barriers (Figure 6).   These barriers form
where headlands are easily erodible and contain
sufficient quantities of sand and gravel for barrier
construction.   Baymouth barriers originate as
spits merging from adjacent, eroding headlands.
The eventual joining of these spits results in a
fairly straight shoreline.

Baymouth barriers are common in microtidal
areas, where the low tidal range (< 6 feet) inhibits
inlets except when breaching occurs during a major
storm.   With the restriction of salt water input,
fresh water or brackish marshes will develop.   The
smaller enclosed embayments are often called salt
ponds, and the barriers are sometimes artificially

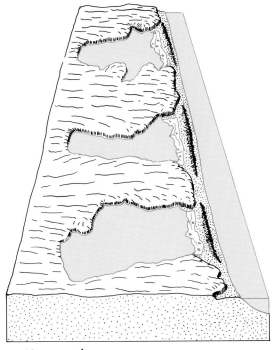

6.   Baymouth Barriers.

opened to improve clam production by maintaining salinity levels. The best examples of baymouth barriers exist along the glaciated coasts of New England, particularly Martha's Vineyard, Massachusetts, and the Rhode Island shoreline.

A tombolo is a special kind of bay barrier which deserves recognition as a separate feature (Figure 7). Tombolos attach an island, usually of glacial or volcanic origin, to the mainland by spit growth. The island, which may be erodible or nonerodible, serves to anchor the barrier. Tombolos

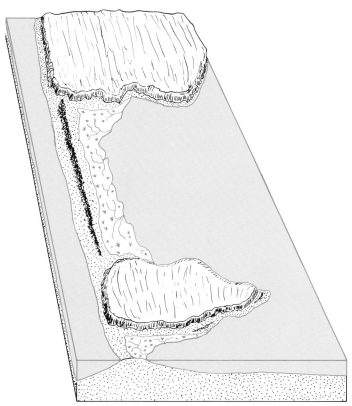

7.   Tombolo.

are most common along the U.S. Northeast glaciated coast where the attached islands are erodible and provide sand for barrier development. The Great Island system and Cape Pogue, Massachusetts, are good examples of tombolos. Large, double tombolos are present along the California coast; here the attached island is a piece of bedrock, forming a promontory.

Barrier Spits

Coastal barriers that are attached at one end to a source of sediment -- mainland or large island -- and extend into open water, are called spits. Barrier spits are formed as longshore currents move abundant sand and gravel from eroding cliffs into open water. Since these sediment-laden currents are directed straight along the shore, material is deposited offshore of shoreline embayments. With the continued delivery of sand, a barrier spit finally forms (see Figure 54). Spits elongate in the general direction of the littoral drift and therefore represent the net movement of sand along a beach. Spits can develop into bay barriers if they grow completely across a bay, or bay barriers can become spits if a permanent inlet is created.

Spits are divided into four types based on their overall shape and position relative to each other. Spits which are relatively straight and narrow are called simple spits (Figure 8). Examples of simple spits include Ogunquit Beach, Maine, and Sandy Neck, Massachusetts.

A double spit develops when there is significant longshore sand transport in both directions along the shoreline (Figure 9). The inlet between the two spit segments is often unstable, migrating laterally in response to the prevailing

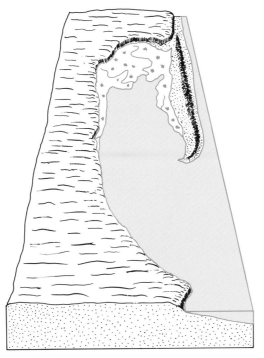

8.   Simple Spit.

several directions.   Sandy Hook, New Jersey, is the classic example of a recurved spit.   In some cases spits can form at the downdrift end of a barrier island; these spits can exhibit large recurvatures, such as Fishing Point at the southern end of Assateague Island, Virginia.

Complex spits are uncommon and only form when both sides of a mainland peninsula are eroding and subject to large enough waves to produce significant longshore sand transport (Figure 11).   The Province Lands of Cape Cod, Massachusetts, formed as a large recurved spit, followed by the growth of an enclosed simple spit.   Due to plentiful sand supply, this complex spit is still prograding at the expense of the eroding glacial cliffs.

direction of net littoral drift.   If the inlet closes, then the double spit is converted into a baymouth barrier.   The inlet will remain open if the tidal exchange between the open ocean and enclosed bay is of sufficient quantity.   Nauset Harbor, Cape Cod, Massachusetts is bounded by a double spit.

Recurved spits are essentially simple spits which are recurved or significantly bent shoreward (Figure 10).   The distinctive recurved dune ridges represent lines of accretion, indicating successive barrier growth.   Recurved spits form when the barrier is significantly influenced by waves from

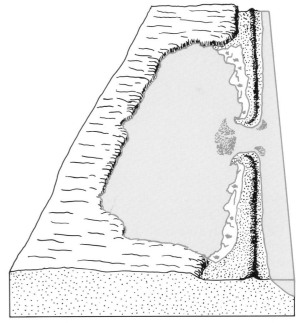

9.   Double Spit.

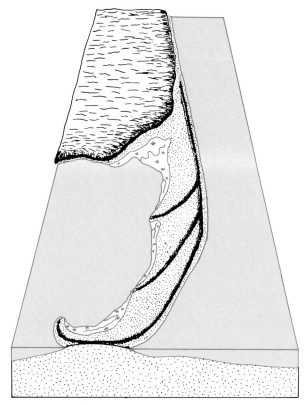

10. Recurved Spit.

Barrier Islands

Barrier islands are the most commonly recognized offshore structures which protect the mainland and enclosed lagoons from direct wave attack by the sea. These islands are the major feature of the coastline from New York to Texas; the United States has the longest and best-developed chain of barrier islands in the world. Consequently it is not surprising that many different types of islands exist. Barrier islands exhibit a wide range in size

and overall shape. This diversity stems from large variations in sand supply, tidal range, and wave energy around the U.S. coastline.

Microtidal barriers (wave-dominated) are found along sandy coastlines with a tidal range less than 6 feet; mesotidal (tide-dominated) barriers are found where the tidal range is between 6 and 12 feet. For tidal ranges above 12 feet (macrotidal conditions), barriers are not expected to form, although it is possible that some small,

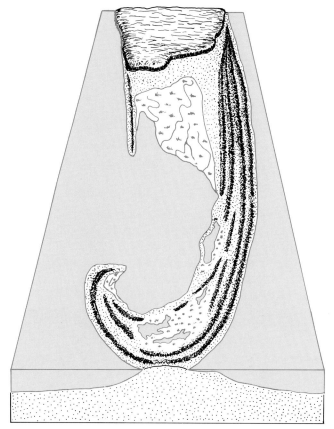

11. Complex Spit.

ephemeral features may exist. In actuality, barrier island morphology depends upon tidal energy in relation to wave energy so that exact boundaries cannot be set by knowledge of tidal range alone. The other variable which plays a principal role in determining barrier expression is sand supply. Utilizing Hayes' micro-meso classification coupled with sediment supply conditions yields four basic types of islands: microtidal transgressive, microtidal regressive, mesotidal transgressive, and mesotidal regressive.

Transgressive indicates sand deficiency and the propensity for shoreline retreat. Regressive denotes accretion, often evidenced by multiple dune ridges. Past accretion does not preclude present or future erosion; a regressive barrier can be converted to a transgressive one with the demise of sufficient sand supplies.

Microtidal transgressive barriers are the least stable and most vulnerable to storm-induced changes of the four island types (Figure 12). These islands, which are long and narrow with few active inlets, are characterized by low-lying topography and numerous washovers, indicating deficient sand supply and relatively rapid shoreline retreat.

Dune stabilization through sand fencing and grass plantings can temporarily convert overwash-susceptible islands into dune-ridge barriers. After dune construction and prevention of overwash, urban development is possible. In some areas, dunes are in disrepair and overwash is regaining importance as an active process, resulting in substantial damage to human structures.

By comparison, microtidal regressive barrier

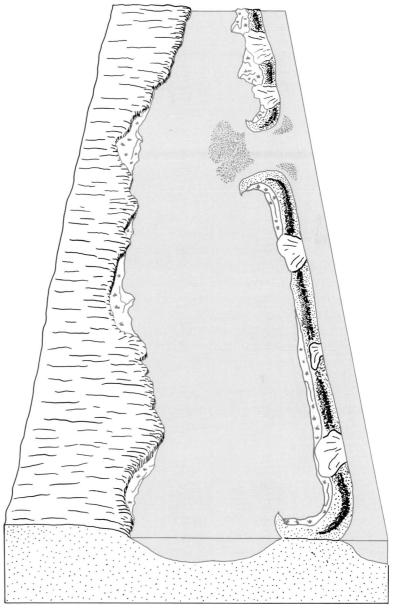

12. Microtidal Transgressive Barrier Island.

islands (Figure 13) often exhibit multiple dune ridges. These ridges are either in parallel (denoting seaward expansion) or arcuate shaped (indicating downdrift accretion). The number and size of dune ridges may be regarded as an index of barrier stability, but some microtidal regressive barriers are still subject to overwash during severe storm conditions.

Microtidal barriers tend to be quite long compared to their width (i.e., Padre Island, Texas, is uninterrupted by natural tidal inlets along its entire 110 mile length). These barriers and associated lagoons are not well adjusted to sudden, major changes in water levels due to the paucity of inlets. With the advent of a storm, the lack of established inlets often results in the breaching of new areas along the barrier island (see Figure 39). Most storm-generated inlets are ephemeral, closing shortly (months to years) afterwards; others may remain open and migrate laterally considerable distances in the direction of net littoral drift. For instance, Fire Island Inlet, New York, migrated 5 miles westward in 115 years before being jettied in 1940. Thus human development on microtidal barriers is often vulnerable to storm damage as well as inlet dynamics. These barriers, particularly the transgressive type, are principally described in this Handbook.

There are numerous examples of microtidal barriers due to the preponderance of low tidal ranges along the U.S. East and Gulf coasts (see Figure 1). Microtidal regressive barriers include the western section of Fire Island, New York, Bogue and Shackleford Banks, North Carolina, and Galveston Island, Texas. Microtidal transgressive barriers are much more numerous due to the historic trend of sea level rise and attendant shore erosion.

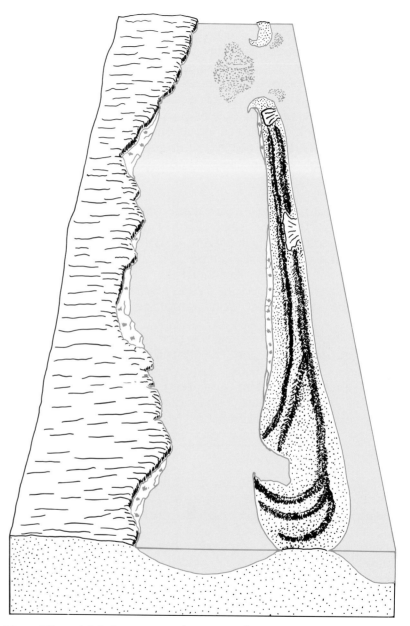

13. Microtidal Regressive Barrier Island.

The Outer Banks of North Carolina are the classic example of this type of barrier chain. Long Beach Island, New Jersey, Fenwick Island, Maryland, Dauphin Island, Alabama, and Padre Island, Texas, are also microtidal transgressive barrier islands. These islands are sometimes referred to as "wash-over barriers", when low and frequently susceptible to overwash activity. Depending upon past uses of the land, type of dune vegetation, and wind regime, a single, often discontinuous barrier dune may be present.

Mesotidal barrier islands are short in length compared to width due to an abundance of tidal inlets, which play a significant role in determining island shape and dynamics. Tidal inlets between mesotidal barriers tend to be much more stable than those in a microtidal setting. While a channel may meander within certain limits, the inlet remains in the same general location. The large tide necessitates many breaks through the barrier chain to allow daily exchange of water between the enclosed bays and the open ocean. Frequently the bays and lagoons are marsh-filled, and the ebb-tidal delta is quite pronounced (Figure 14).

Many mesotidal regressive barrier islands tend to have a drumstick shape with a bulbous updrift end, tapering to a multiple dune ridge central section, and terminating in a series of arcuate-shaped dune ridges (Figure 15). This characteristic drumstick shape is reflective of the relative stability of different parts of the island. The bulbous updrift end is subject to erosional and accretionary trends depending upon orientation of the inlet channel and position of the ebb tidal delta (Figure 15). Presence of a bulge denotes accretion, but storm-induced realignment of the inlet channel can eliminate the seaward

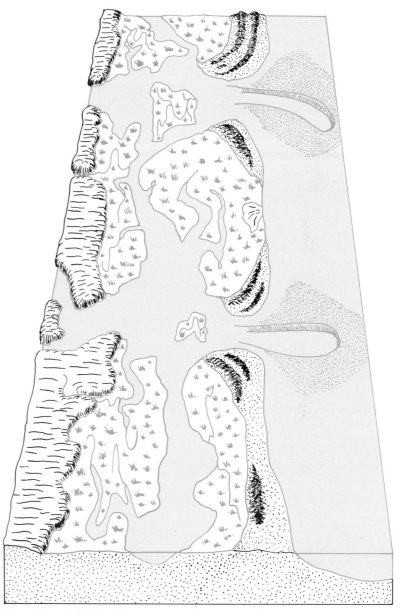

14. Mesotidal Transgressive Barrier Island.

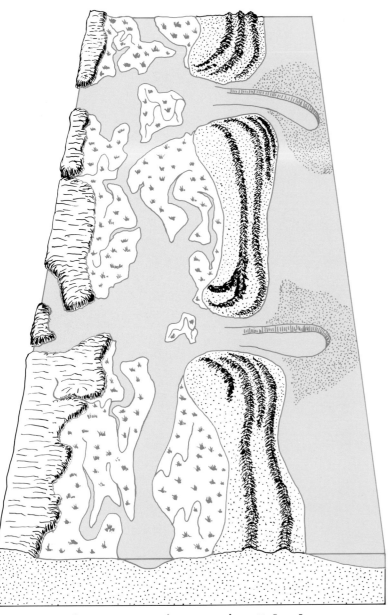

15. Mesotidal Regressive Barrier Island.

offset. The central section is the most stable part of a mesotidal island. The recurved downdrift end is the result of spit accretion, but this section may be subject to inlet severance if the barrier has been overextended.

Mesotidal transgressive barrier islands are characterized by marshy plains and remnant beach ridges. Although not common, examples include Morris and Capers Islands in South Carolina. Mesotidal regressive barrier islands include Plum Island, Massachusetts, Kiawah and Bulls Islands, South Carolina. Mesotidal drumstick-shaped barrier islands have also been found in Alaska and the Netherlands.

Barriers in microtidal environments can some-times assume mesotidal characteristics, such as the rapidly transgressing Virginia barrier islands. The huge bulbous updrift end of Parramore Island, Virginia, is indicative of drumstick barriers, and the adjacent Wachapreague Inlet has been shown to play the major role in altering the shape of the island. Wachapreague Inlet has remained open in approximately the same position during historical time, resulting in marsh-filled lagoons and a well developed ebb tidal delta; this typifies mesotidal inlet behavior.

Research suggests that Wachapreague Inlet and the other major inlets along the Virginia barrier chain are controlled by the inherited topography. In short, tidal inlet position is fixed by earlier (Pleistocene) riverine drainage courses, which have provided the path of least resistance for rising waters and inlet position. Inlet main-tenance and existence through a barrier chain is virtually assured by these subsurface controls. Artificially stabilized microtidal inlets can also acquire some mesotidal characteristics after a long period of time. For instance, Ocean City Inlet, Maryland, has developed an immense ebb tidal delta in less than 50 years after jetty construction. These examples demonstrate the dominant role that tidal inlets play in barrier island morphology and dynamics. In turn, tidal inlet hydraulics are primarily controlled by tidal range.

A subset of the typical mesotidal barrier island is represented by St. Phillips Island, South Carolina (Figure 16). This barrier appears as a series of low, vegetated beach ridges surrounded by a marshy plain. The present morphology indicates a geologic history of ample sand supply, permitting serial ridge development. Presence of the salt marsh along the ocean shoreline suggests that the primary barrier ridge protecting these backbarrier environments has already been eroded away, indicating the recent transgressive nature of the shoreline. This case points out the complexity of barrier forms, and the geomorphic information necessary to unravel their geologic development. The major advantage of the micro-meso, transgressive-regressive classification scheme lies in its predictive ability regarding dynamic barrier behavior with respect to human development.

There are three other types of barrier structures that deserve attention: capes, sea islands, and cheniers. Barrier islands that project into the sea to form right-angled shorelines are called cuspate forelands or capes (Figure 17). The origin of capes is still much in debate; Cape Henlopen, Delaware, clearly developed as a spit feature. The large recurved spit at the southern end of Assateague Island, Virginia, may someday be named Cape Chincoteague instead of Fishing Point. Other

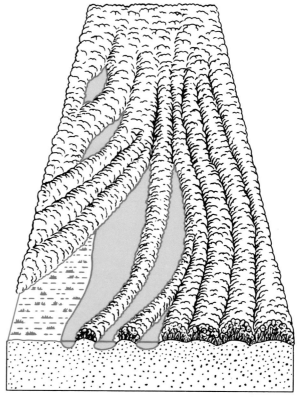

16. Beach Ridge Island.

capes, such as Capes Hatteras, Lookout, and Fear along the Outer Banks of North Carolina, are much larger features, and their origin may be traced back to much earlier times and seaward position on the shelf as previously explained.

Cuspate forelands typically consist of transgressive and regressive sections. For instance, the north trending flank of Cape Hatteras, North Carolina, is long and narrow and often subject to overwash (Figure 17). Human development located

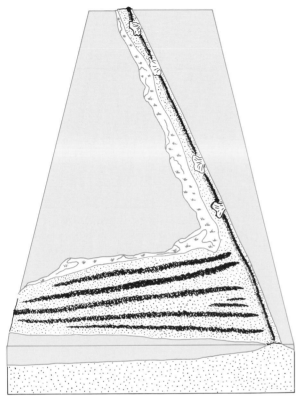

17. Cape.

Sea islands are only found in a few regions along the U.S. coastline; Georgia is known as the sea island coast. These large islands consist of two parts: a recent or Holocene outer barrier and a Pleistocene core (Figure 18). The outer barrier may be welded onto the Pleistocene core or separated from it by intervening salt marshes and tidal creeks. Only the outer barrier structure behaves in a dynamic manner. The island core is Pleistocene in age (approximately 100,000 years old), is quite high (often above the 100 year and sometimes above the 500 year floodplain level), and covered by a mature, thick continental soil which supports a

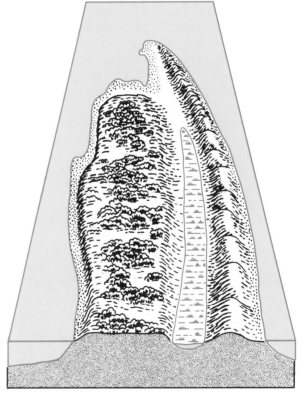

in these areas is subject to severe damage during coastal storms. By contrast, the southern flank is generally accretionary in nature, resulting in a spectacular array of parallel to subparallel dune ridges. In fact, the cape nucleus largely consists of these accretionary dune ridges with intervening lowlands (swales). In addition to the often noted Carolina capes, Capes Canaveral and Blas in Florida and Cape Romain in Georgia are well known.

18. Sea Island.

climax maritime forest. Thus, the Pleistocene core, which can be quite large in areal dimensions, is actually a very stable feature and is merely an immersed piece of the mainland. Examples of sea islands include Hilton Head Island, South Carolina, Cumberland Island, Georgia and Amelia Island, Florida.

Cheniers, the lowest and most vulnerable to storm surges of all barrier types, are generally strandplains (low-lying mainland areas), instead of true barrier structures (Figure 19). Cheniers consist largely of organic deposits (salt marshes)

with ridges of sand and silt overlying this basal structure. Chenier comes form the French word meaning oak, and many of the larger ridges are covered with live oak trees. These marshy plains with low sandy/shelly beach ridges are often merely seaward extensions of the mainland. While salt marshes and shallow lakes are incorporated into this landform, it is often impossible to define a landward margin without relying upon artificial canals and waterways.

Cheniers are best developed along the west Louisiana-east Texas coastline, downdrift of the silt-laden Mississippi River, which serves as the sediment source. Growth of the marshy seaward edge of a chenier is reflective of excessive sediment that waves are unable to move alongshore or offshore. During major hurricanes, severe erosion and extensive flooding of the chenier occurs, sometimes forming the characteristic elongated beach ridges. Cameron, Louisiana, is built upon a chenier plain.

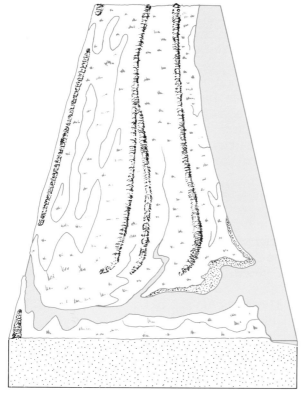

19. Chenier.

Barrier Environments

A barrier system includes the beach, dunes, flats, and marshes (Figure 20). Each of these geomorphic elements has a characteristic morphology. The beach responds to changing energy conditions on a daily or even hourly basis. The berm is the region most directly affected by waves during storms and therefore is quite unstable. The berm grades into the foredune (Figure 22), but in some cases the berm may not exist.

The dune zone may consist of a single ridge, several parallel ridges, or a number of curving lines, stabilized by beach grass. There may also be an open dune region without distinctive lines, and the dune zone may extend as far as the intertidal zone (area between high and low tide) on the bayside or grade into the barrier flats. Those islands that are subject to periodic or regular overwash tend to be dominated by scattered dunes with extensive barrier flats.

The barrier flat, a result of overwash or inlet processes, is an extensive plain that can support grasslands, shrub-thickets or woodlands, but is primarily dominated by grassland communities. Where dune development allows for a degree of stability, woodlands and forests can grow.

On the bayside of a barrier is the intertidal zone, which is divided into two topographically distinctive parts. The high marsh is the region of the intertidal zone that ranges from the highest tides (spring) to the smallest tides (neap); the low marsh extends from the high marsh to mean sea level or slightly below.

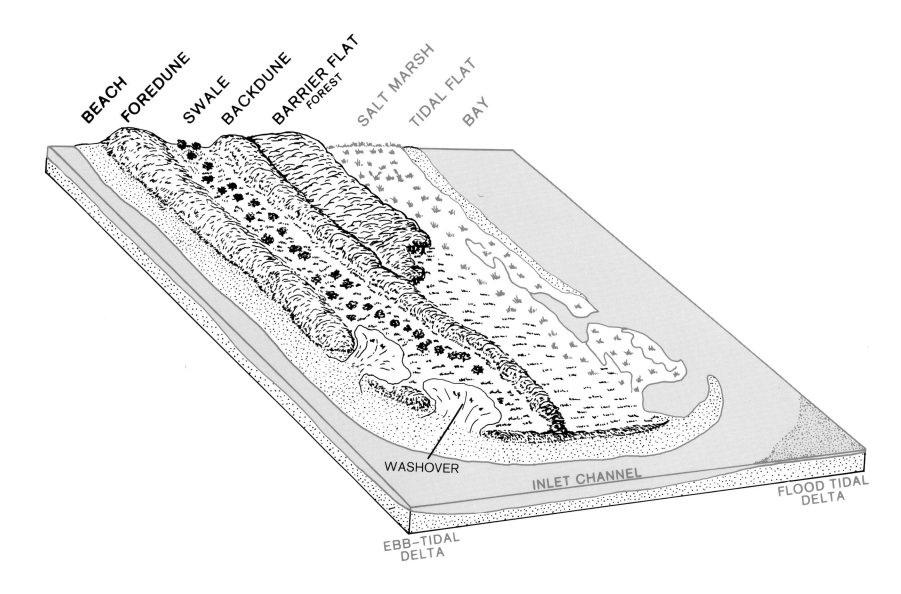

BEACH FOREDUNE SWALE BACKDUNE BARRIER FLAT FOREST SALT MARSH TIDAL FLAT BAY

WASHOVER

INLET CHANNEL

EBB-TIDAL DELTA

FLOOD TIDAL DELTA

20. Barrier Environments.

Barrier islands are dominated by the marine environment, which extends to the upper tidal levels. The seaward limit of the nearshore zone (e.g., where waves cease to scour the bottom) is more difficult to define. On some barrier coasts, such as those with broad continental shelves, large storm waves can stir bottom sediments all the way to the outer edge of the shelf. In this case a strict interpretation of the nearshore zone would require inclusion of the entire continental shelf (several hundred miles offshore). For describing typical nearshore processes, however, the depth of wave base and thus the seaward limit of the nearshore zone is generally set at 30 feet of water.

There is appreciable sediment transport in the nearshore zone due to waves striking the shoreline at an angle; this longshore sediment transport can be compared to a conveyor belt. The cumulative effect of continuously breaking waves is to generate a steady, sediment-laden longshore current. The direction of transport is determined by the direction of wave approach relative to the shoreline. Wave conditions, however, change almost constantly so that the quantity and direction of the longshore sediment transport (littoral drift) must also change. During storm conditions, longshore currents can be very strong (velocities of several feet per second). As this sediment is moved alongshore, it can be interrupted by littoral barriers such as groins, jetties and inlets.

In addition to longshore currents, water and sediment can be directed offshore by rip currents as part of the nearshore circulation system (Figure 21). Rip currents, sometimes confused with the mythical "undertow," can be quite strong during high surf conditions.

21. Turbulent head of a rip current is shown moving offshore into deep water.

Beach

A beach can be defined as an accumulation of wave-washed, loose sediment that extends between the outermost breakers and the landward limit of wave and swash action. A generalized beach profile and related terminology are shown in Figure 22. The beach is generally composed of the foreshore, the portion sloping toward the ocean, and the backshore, the portion of the beach from the berm crest to the dunes.

Where waves break offshore, submerged ridges or bars of coarse sediment are present. Most waves break at the inner bar that parallels the shore of a barrier island, but some smaller waves may not break until reaching the water's edge. Bars, by definition, are submerged at all tides. A longshore feature that becomes exposed at low tide is called a ridge. The trough between the ridge and beach berm is termed a runnel. Ridges and runnels are commonly found along mesotidal coasts, such as Cape Cod, Massachusetts.

Ridges can migrate landward by swash action and eventually weld onto the beach face. Submarine bars become ridges as they migrate into the inter-

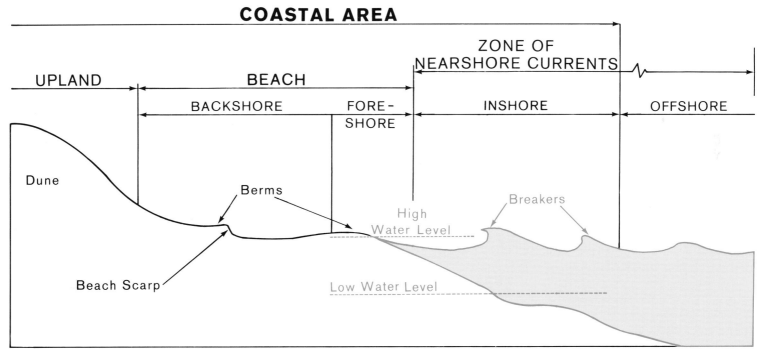

22.   Beach Terminology.

tidal zone where their sand serves to nourish and rebuild the berm. This process often occurs after storms and is a principal means of beach recovery.

Upon breaking, waves are translated into swash, which is a thin sheet of water flowing over the beach face. Swash consists of two motions: the uprush created by initial wave break and the backwash that occurs as the water returns seaward. When waves approach at right angles to the shore, the uprush flows straight up the sloping beach face, slows to a stop, and under gravity flows straight back down the slope as backwash. During oblique wave approach, the uprush travels diagonally up the beach face, but the backwash flows straight down the slope. The swash moves in a sawtooth fashion on the beach foreshore, resulting in the longshore movement of sand particles. This process is a secondary mechanism of littoral drift of beach sediment (see Nearshore section).

The swash process results in sediment accretion, creating a berm (Figure 22). The berm represents a change in slope from the seaward face of the foreshore to the gentle landward inclination of the backshore. Some beaches have no berms; others exhibit one or multiple (generally summer and winter) berms. The crest of a berm may rise several feet above the high water level. The height limitation for a berm is determined by wave size; large swell waves can build substantial berms. Severe storms, however, often result in beach erosion with berm flattening.

Rapid transport of sediment on- and offshore reflects changes in energy conditions, principally wave height. The beach profile adjusts to the wave energy supplied in order to achieve "equilibrium" conditions. In general, high waves with short periods cause the beach to erode, and the berm sand is shifted offshore. Low waves with longer periods, primarily in summer, move sand from the bar and return it to the berm. The average wave height varies on a seasonal basis, resulting in typical "winter" (high energy) and "summer" (low energy) beach profiles. The winter profile is characterized by a narrow backshore, flat foreshore, and a large offshore bar. The summer profile has a wide backshore, a steep foreshore, and a well-developed berm. These profiles are only related to season in that most storms along the U.S. East coast occur in the winter.

Although adjustment to an equilibrium profile takes place continuously with the tidal cycle and seasonally, large-scale changes are most evident during a coastal storm (Figure 23). Short, high storm waves (termed sea) flatten the beach profile, remove the berm and sometimes form a scarp. A large storm bar, which serves as a storage area for much of the sand, develops offshore as the foreshore erodes. This submarine feature acts as a wave filter so that less energy actually reaches the beach face.

With more intense storms, the barrier dunes may be eroded and breached by overwash surges (see Figure 35). Erosion is associated with passage of winter northeasters or infrequent hurricanes (see Storm section). Beach changes take place within a very short time interval, lasting from only one-half a tidal cycle to several days. Swell (sometimes called ground swell) usually follows sea conditions as a low pressure cell (coastal storm) moves along and/or offshore. The swell moves the sand back onshore, often by the process of ridge and runnel migration as previously described.

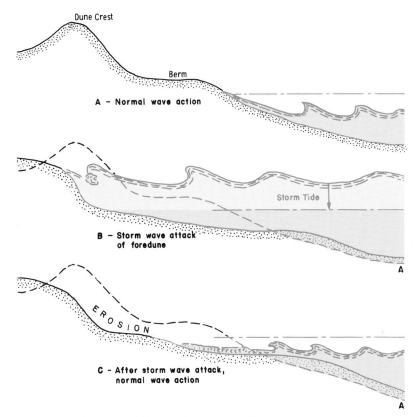

Dune Crest

Berm

A - Normal wave action

Storm Tide

B - Storm wave attack of foredune

A

E R O S I O N

C - After storm wave attack, normal wave action

A

23. Beach profile changes in response to a coastal storm.

From the berm crest to the toe of the primary dune is the zone termed the beach backshore. This area is rarely subject to hydraulic (water) action, except during extremely high spring tides or coastal storm activity. Organic debris collects in this zone, forming drift lines (see Figure 69). Contained in this debris are the broken rhizomes (underground runners) of American beach grass and seeds of sea rocket and seaside goldenrod. Aeolian (wind-blown) sand may accumulate around the drift

lines, which can grow to form new barrier dunes (see Figure 30). However, the erosional tendency for most barrier islands precludes the long-term accretion of sediment necessary for the growth of new major dune lines.

During oblique wave approach, the longshore current can become quite swift (3-4 feet per second), resulting in erosion of the beach face and producing a vertical scarp (Figure 24). In this fashion a wide berm may disappear within a few hours. As soon as the oblique wave attack stops, scarp retreat ceases. The scarp can later be buried by berm accretion.

24. Beach scarp is in the process of forming due to swash grazing of the berm at Fire Island, New York.

Frequently, cusps are a distinctive feature of the beach. The beach surface is crenulated, characterized by an evenly spaced series of rounded, small headlands and bays known as beach cusps (Figure 25). The horizontal spacing of cusps ranges from a few feet to hundreds of feet, and their local relief varies from a few inches to several feet. Several kinds of these rhythmic beach forms have been described, but their origin is still the subject of much debate. It is known that the cusp patterns can migrate along the beach, depending on wave approach. When waves strike the beach obliquely, cusps are usually destroyed.

Sand waves, which are much larger features than beach cusps, have also been observed along

26. Large sand waves are prominent at Cape Hatteras, North Carolina.

some barrier shorelines (Figure 26). Movement of sand waves downdrift results in erosion periods alternating with periods of accretion at a point along the shore. Since sand waves migrate slowly along the shore, beach erosion (associated with the sand wave trough) and beach accretion (corresponding to the sand wave crest) at any point may be years apart.

25. Beach cusps at Nauset Spit, Cape Cod.

27. Development of curvilinear beach ridges on an accreting spit.

Beach ridges are a type of storm berm formed by waves and swash; therefore they generally exhibit little relief. In some cases beach ridges are capped by wind-blown (aeolian) sand; these accretionary features are called dune ridges. As discussed in the next section, dunes are formed by accretion of wind-blown sand, and barrier dunes can reach heights greater than 10 meters.

The mechanism for building beach ridges on an accreting sand spit is biogeological in nature. As the spit grows into open water, an above-water platform results from wave and current transport of sediment. Beachgrass fragments and the seeds of other beach plants are transported to the crest of this feature by spit washover.

The plants grow up from the buried drift lines, where the rotting remains of algae and other plants provide initial nutrients, and soon are large enough to trap both aeolian and water-deposited sand. As the ridge builds around the plants, upward accretion still maintains the general pattern of the initial drift line deposit. These lines are frequently present on the backshore in curving arcs along an accreting barrier spit. The beach ridge is curvilinear in form since it conforms to the beach arc (Figure 27). As the beach builds in an accreting system, the next series of drift lines will also be curvilinear. The end result is a barrier spit with distinctive beach ridge arcs on which upland vegetation can survive, with interdunal low areas that support wetland species (Figure 28).

28. Beach ridges (shown as white lines) are separated by interdunal lakes and wetlands at the terminus of Monomoy Island, Massachusetts.

Dunes

Without the development of dunes, sand accretion can proceed only as high as the storm surge can reach. Vegetation is critical in dune building and stabilization; otherwise, the sand would continue moving as it does in the desert. After sand is deposited on the beach backshore by waves, the winds take over and either move the sand inland or back out to sea, depending on the prevailing wind direction. Wind velocities of 12 mph or greater are capable of moving fine, dried beach sand.

Formation of dune lines is dependent upon direction of prevailing winds relative to the orientation of the barrier. Fairweather (prevailing) winds move more sand than do storm (dominant) winds, since storms are infrequent and generally accompanied by rain. Where strong winds are on-shore, such as at Padre Island, Texas, large dunes can quickly form. Where winds are alongshore or offshore, dune lines tend to be lower and more open.

The height of the dune is controlled primarily by sand size and wind velocity, whereas seaward dune vegetation growth is controlled by wave action and soil salinity. The seaward dune position also depends upon the frequency of storms eroding the dune face and the rate at which these scarps can heal by wind transport and vegetation growth.

Sand transported over the dune crest results in landward movement of this feature. On eroding shorelines, dune system survival depends upon the relative rates of dune migration and shoreline retreat. During periods of increased shoreline erosion, the dunes may be eroded and breached during storm conditions.

Because coastal dune ridges do not develop uniformly, dune topography can be quite irregular. Wind can be concentrated in lower areas, resulting in a blowout (Figure 29). A dune ridge, usually an effective barrier to storm waves, can be breached by overwash surges at these weakened areas in the dune line. New embryonic dunes can then form in the dune breach or on the washover fan.

One important feature in the dune building process is the presence of vegetation, particularly

29. Blowout in the barrier dune at Nauset Spit, Cape Cod, Massachusetts.

dune grasses: American beach grass (Ammophila) in the U.S. Northeast and sea oats (Uniola paniculata) in the U.S. Southeast and Gulf coasts. These grasses, which have the ability to tolerate salt spray and sand burial, are largely responsible for building dunes and stabilizing the sand.

Wind velocities are greatly diminished upon entering the blades of grass. Because the carrying capacity of the wind is reduced, the blowing sand is deposited in the grass. This sand pileup would soon bury all nonadaptive plants. However, beach grass plants have the ability to grow upward with accumulating sand so that the dune can build higher and be relatively stable throughout this sequence of development (Figure 30). As the dunes grow higher and wider, they coalesce to form a dune line with an axis parallel to the shoreline.

Eventually the dune will be invaded by other plants which add to the vegetative cover. Many of these species are nitrogen-fixing plants, such as bayberry and beach pea, which help to support other plants by adding needed nitrates to the barren sand. With increasing stability, soil development, and protection from salt spray, shrub thickets and eventually woodlands will develop (Figure 31).

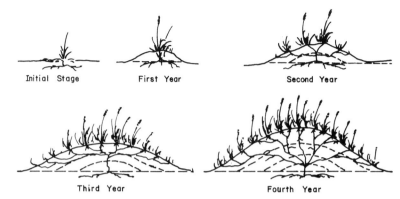

Initial Stage   First Year   Second Year

Third Year   Fourth Year

30. Growth and development of a beach grass dune from a drift line deposit.

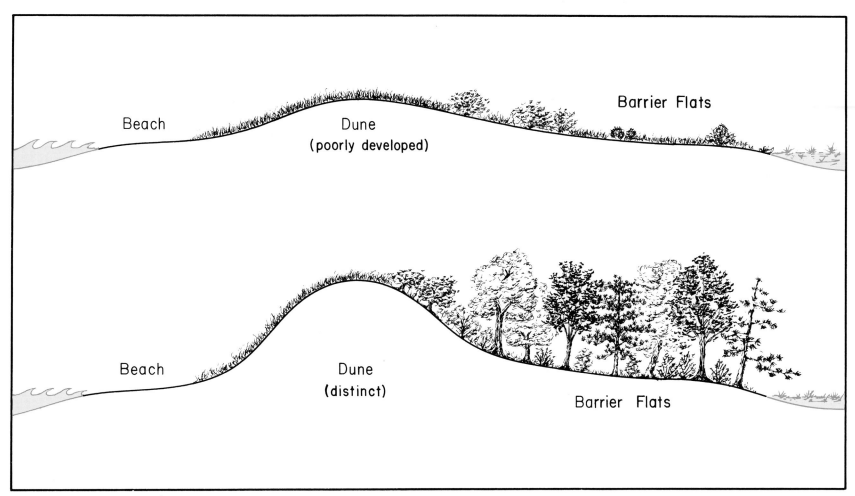

Beach

Dune
(poorly developed)

Barrier Flats

Beach

Dune
(distinct)

Barrier Flats

31. Cross-sections across a barrier dune illustrating changes in vegetation due to differences in dune development. The poorly developed dune may be in a stage of early development or may not evolve to maturity due to rapid beach erosion and overwash.

Freshwater Wetlands

Freshwater habitats are characterized by little to no salinity and are generally not influenced by the tide. Rainfall and snow are the only sources to maintain standing water areas and the groundwater table on barrier islands. Freshwater ponds are small and can be classed according to their mode of origin into two basic groups: (1) dune ponds in low areas (slacks or swales) between sand dunes, and (2) coastal ponds created by the closing of a former bay or lagoon.

Slacks are low areas or depressions between dunes created by windblown sand movement or human activity. The most common means of dune slack formation is through wind deflation forming a blowout (Figure 29). Deflation and hence depression deepening can occur until the groundwater level is reached. Dune slacks are therefore generally moist or wet areas due to their relatively low elevation. During rainy periods the whole depression can be flooded, creating a temporary dune pond. In some cases, these depressions are permanently flooded and standing water exists year round.

Freshwater wetlands (Figure 32) are controlled by the level of the water lens (or groundwater)

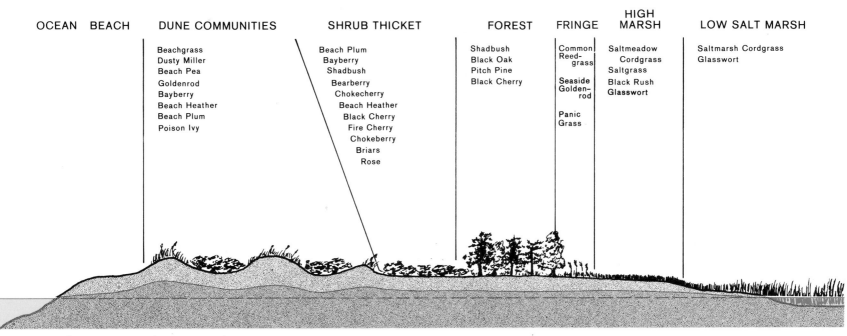

OCEAN BEACH	DUNE COMMUNITIES	SHRUB THICKET	FOREST	FRINGE	HIGH MARSH	LOW SALT MARSH
	Beachgrass Dusty Miller Beach Pea Goldenrod Bayberry Beach Heather Beach Plum Poison Ivy	Beach Plum Bayberry Shadbush Bearberry Chokecherry Beach Heather Black Cherry Fire Cherry Chokeberry Briars Rose	Shadbush Black Oak Pitch Pine Black Cherry	Common Reed-grass Seaside Golden-rod Panic Grass	Saltmeadow Cordgrass Saltgrass Black Rush Glasswort	Saltmarsh Cordgrass Glasswort

32. Barrier vegetation zonation for U.S. Northeast coast.

beneath the dunes. The island water table can be envisioned as a lens of fresh water floating on salt water within the porous material of the barrier subsurface. Because of the difference in densities between fresh and salty water, the fresh water lens behaves like an iceberg, extending forty feet below sea level for every foot of fresh water above sea level (Figure 33). Rain is the only source for recharging island groundwater, which flows downward and laterally under its own weight. This one-way flow of water prevents the salt water from intruding into surface layers where high chlorinity would kill the terrestrial plants. Overpumping of the groundwater in excess of recharge by precipitation can significantly lower the water table and eventually draw the salt water inland. Changes in this groundwater level will be reflected in the extent and health of the freshwater communities.

Vegetation typical of freshwater environments includes grasses, rushes, sedges, and cattails. Many interdune slacks have limited drainage, and low-oxygen (acidic) conditions develop. These conditions foster the development of heath and sphagnum moss communities, similar to those found in bogs.

Barrier Flats

Barrier flats are those sections of an island that have little relief, often lying less than 5 feet above mean water level. These flattened areas on the backdune area can result when washovers destroy the dune ridge topography.

Dunes are the major topographic feature of the U.S. Northeast barrier systems; barrier flats are restricted in areal extent. In some cases, dunes and salt marshes share a common border, and no true flats exist, as is the case on parts of Nauset Spit, Cape Cod, Massachusetts. However, U.S. mid-Atlantic and Southeastern barriers are more typically broad and low and have extensive flats. The dominant topographic feature on many of these microtidal barriers is a flat grassy plain, produced by overwash. The formation of these flats is tied to the storm surges that erode dune ridges and deposit sand in low areas, effectively leveling the topography.

Barrier flats covered with grassland or meadow vegetation are adapted to frequent sand burial and flooding by overwash. One of the most important species here is salt meadow cordgrass (Spartina patens). Sand deposited by overwash on these vegetated flats is quickly colonized by marsh grasses growing up through the overlying sediments.

With decreasing overwash frequency, either because of upward dune growth or lack of storms, barrier flats will support thickets, followed by woodlands and finally forest (Figures 32 and 33).

The woody vegetation usually starts on the backside of the flat near the salt marsh border and grows seaward as dune development allows for greater stability and protection from salt spray.

Maritime forests are an important component of the barrier island ecosystem (Figure 34). Forests can develop on barrier flats in the lee of protective foredunes or on backbarrier, secondary dunes. Maritime forests are not present on narrow, unstable barriers such as Nauset Spit, Massachusetts; they are restricted to the wider and more protected portions of islands. The Colonial settlements along the Outer Banks of North Carolina were located in the maritime forest because it is the highest and safest place to live on a barrier island.

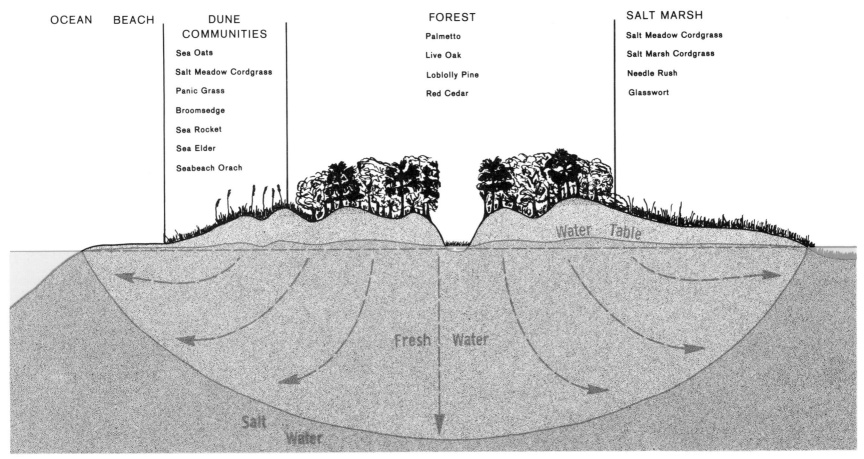

OCEAN BEACH	DUNE COMMUNITIES	FOREST	SALT MARSH
	Sea Oats	Palmetto	Salt Meadow Cordgrass
	Salt Meadow Cordgrass	Live Oak	Salt Marsh Cordgrass
	Panic Grass	Loblolly Pine	Needle Rush
	Broomsedge	Red Cedar	Glasswort
	Sea Rocket		
	Sea Elder		
	Seabeach Orach		

33. Barrier vegetation zonation for U.S. Southeast coast. Fresh groundwater lens is also shown.

34. The Sunken Forest at Fire Island National Seashore, New York.

Washover fans are created by the flow of water through the primary dune line with sand deposition on the barrier flats, marsh or into the lagoon, depending on storm magnitude and island width (Figures 35 and 36). Overwash is defined as any swash uprush that crosses a dune line (or storm berm, if no dunes are present). Usually overwash occurs during coastal storms, but a marginal event can occur at low areas in the barrier dune line when large breaking waves coincide with a high spring tide.

Storm overwash can occur through narrow dune gaps, over wide sections with low dune topography, or across an entire stretch of a barrier island. The shape and dimension of the washover deposit is determined by backshore topography and volume of sediment being introduced by the overwash surges. Large washover fans can terminate in the lagoon or bay behind the barrier system (Figure 36). If scouring of the barrier proceeds to an elevation below mean sea level, an inlet can result.

If the dune ridge is continuous and of sufficient elevation, storm waves will not be able to penetrate it. Overwash generally occurs where the dune system has been weakened, either naturally by blowouts or artificially by humans. Depressions in the ridge front, especially vehicle crossovers, serve as passageways for flood waters during storms. Overwash surges pass through these breaches and excavate the dune base by lateral undercutting. In this fashion, the washovers will become larger at the expense of the barrier dunes.

35. Overwash surge crossing the breach in the barrier dune line at Assateague Island, Maryland.

Where the barrier is wide with extensive barrier flats or salt marshes, washovers rather than inlets will generally occur. Overwash surges quickly lose their initial, high velocities due to percolation and frictional effects as the bore of water crosses the barrier flats. Hence erosion is minimized and sand deposition occurs in the fan (Figure 36) as the surge energy drops to a low level.

Revegetation of barren washover flats progresses rapidly after the dune line has been restored. From field inspection it is sometimes difficult to identify old washover areas, but their existence can often be verified by using historical aerial photography. Although the dune breach may be repaired, the fan feature and vegetation zonation of the barrier flats will still be apparent.

36. The February 6-7, 1978 northeaster resulted in overwash deposition into Pleasant Bay at several localities along Nauset Spit, Massachusetts.

As a barrier spit grows into open water, it provides protection for ecosystems that require quiet water, such as tidal flats and salt marshes. These intertidal environments are built from sands, muds, and clays transported through tidal inlets or across the barrier for deposition in the enclosed bay. Through time the sea bottom is shoaled, extending the intertidal zone and providing new substrate for salt marsh expansion. Marsh grasses gradually stabilize this surface by spreading outward onto the tidal flats. Salt marsh development in the lee of a protective barrier has been well documented by Redfield for Barnstable Marsh (see Figure 54).

Most of our Nation's tidal wetlands have been built upon river sediments deposited into shallow coastal waters. The Mississippi River delta is an excellent example of this kind of marsh development. Along the mainland bayshore, marshes have generally formed by land submergence with sea level rise. This process of upland conversion to salt marshes is particularly evident along Pamlico Sound, North Carolina, where pine trees are dying on the margins of invading salt marshes. Along the barrier bayside, inlets, overwash, and aeolian processes have played varying roles in promoting new salt marsh growth.

When inlets open, sandy shoals develop in the bay. These shoals (flood tidal deltas) provide substrate for new salt marshes after the inlet closes or migrates downdrift (see Figure 56).

Marsh that grows close to active inlets or accreting spits is most productive due to continual flushing by tidal currents. While inlets are the most important source of new intertidal areas for marsh colonization, major washover deposits can also serve in this capacity. Salt marshes can form on the backside of barriers when overwash surges carry sand directly into a lagoon. In some cases, older marshes are buried by overwash sand, but new, more productive marshes will form along the bay edge. Aeolian processes may be responsible for sand transport into a bay on a site-specific basis, but are generally insignificant on most barriers.

Physical processes create the environmental setting requisite for marsh establishment and also largely determine their biological characteristics. Considering the variation in geophysical phenomena, it is surprising to find the same salt marsh species along the entire U.S. East and Gulf coasts. The inability of other plants to cope with the severe stresses of tidal flooding and salt water immersion has left the marsh zone free to relatively few salt tolerant species (halophytes).

Coastal marsh vegetation displays zonation with respect to elevation, and can be divided into two topographically distinctive parts (Figure 37). The low marsh is dominated by salt marsh cordgrass (Spartina alterniflora), which is found from approximately mean sea level upward to the mean high tide. This tall, hardy grass, which is the most productive member of the marsh community, often forms a narrow vegetated band along tidal creeks. Where marginal areas are shallow or tides large, Spartina alterniflora forms extensive marsh-lands.

The high marsh occupies the intertidal region

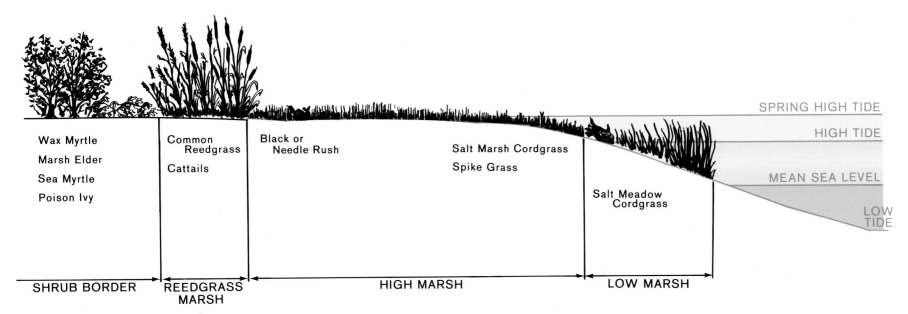

Labels on figure:

SPRING HIGH TIDE
HIGH TIDE
MEAN SEA LEVEL
LOW TIDE

Wax Myrtle
Marsh Elder
Sea Myrtle
Poison Ivy

Common Reedgrass
Cattails

Black or Needle Rush

Salt Marsh Cordgrass
Spike Grass

Salt Meadow Cordgrass

SHRUB BORDER | REEDGRASS MARSH | HIGH MARSH | LOW MARSH

37. Salt Marsh Zonation.

that flourishes at the mean high tide level. Salt meadow cordgrass (Spartina patens) dominates this region, often forming extensive flat marshy platforms. Also present are spike grass (Distichlis spicata) and black rush (Juncus gerardi) in the North and needle rush (Juncus roemerianus) in the South. The high marsh is completely flooded only during spring tides and storms.

A large amount of marsh productivity is tied up in underlying organic peat deposits. Dead organic matter, along with fine silts and clays screened from the water column by the grass swards, results in the upward accretion of the marsh surface. This nearly horizontal plain of the high marsh forms a level which coincides closely with the mean high-tide mark. The high marsh builds upward through time and has the unique ability to maintain its relative elevation in concert with slowly rising sea levels.

Because of the cohesive nature of peat deposits, salt marshes are very resistant to erosion, even when subjected to storm-generated currents and breaking waves. Older marshes behind barriers in a large bay, however, can be slowly eroded by bank collapse (scarping) with continual wave action. Where significant wave action or tidal currents occur along a bay margin of the barrier, sandy intertidal flats exist. Tidal flats are well developed in areas with large tidal ranges, such as Cape Cod Bay and other mesotidal embayments. In a microtidal environment, the flats exposed at low tide occur as a narrow strip around the edge of the salt marsh, except near inlets where currents prevent colonization by Spartina alterniflora.

Separating the individual islands of a barrier chain are inlets through which tidal currents exchange water with the backbarrier lagoons (Figure 38). Inlets are also the primary means by which sand is transported landward across a migrating barrier system. They open and close in response to changing conditions and may migrate long distances along a barrier shoreline. For instance, Fire Island Inlet, New York, migrated 5 miles westward between 1825 and 1940. An inlet may approach equilibrium conditions if a balance is achieved between tidal currents that scour the channel and the longshore transport of sand that tends to close an inlet. These factors are constantly adjusting as an inlet cuts deeper or wider, builds shoals or changes configuration.

Inlet stability is related to the strength of the longshore current versus the tidal jet flushing capacity. Inlets along microtidal coasts tend to close unless there is substantial outflow of water from a major river. Dredging is often necessary in order to maintain a navigable channel through a barrier island. Attempts to stabilize inlet channels by jetties have often led to severe difficulties (erosion and deposition of adjacent shores) and continued dredging operations are usually necessary.

When open, an inlet acts as a complete or partial barrier to longshore sediment transport. Depending on equilibrium conditions, an inlet may trap sand or naturally bypass a large portion of the sediment in the littoral drift system. Under the conditions of small tidal flows and high rates of littoral drift, an inlet will eventually close.

Use of the term "inlet" to describe the openings between barrier islands is somewhat of a misnomer since they are also "outlets" for lagoonal and estuarine waters. Inlets are often created when storm tides force water across a barrier, elevating the water level in a bay. As a storm moves northward, the trapped bay water is forced seaward by a change in hurricane force winds, breaching the barrier from the lagoonal side (Figure 39). An inlet results if the channel is cut below mean sea level and allows for free exchange of ocean and bay water. Inlets along microtidal barrier coasts are relatively nonpermanent features since they tend to migrate laterally in response to longshore sediment transport and storm wave approach. Therefore, inlets along these coasts are highly unstable and rather unpredictable; areas adjacent to these features should be avoided as sites for human development.

Inlets consist of several distinctive parts, the most conspicuous being the throat--the breach in the barrier structure. The dimensions of this opening are dependent on the area of the enclosed bay or lagoon and the tidal range. On the seaward side of the inlet are a series of shoals called the ebb tide delta, marked by breaking waves. This feature is usually not well developed in microtidal settings because of constant erosion and reworking by ocean waves. The ebb tidal delta is formed from the sand that moves through the inlet with the ebbing tide. This delta serves as a natural sediment bypass system as sand moves underwater from one side of the inlet to the other.

38. The New England Blizzard of 1978 created a new tidal inlet, splitting Monomoy into two islands.

With a rising tide, sand that has been moving along the beach as littoral drift is interrupted by the tidal current; a portion of this material will be transported through the inlet for deposition in the bay. This sedimentation produces an extensive flood tidal delta that exhibits a deltaic pattern when fully developed (see Figure 55). With inlet closure or migration, the flood tidal delta becomes prime substrate for salt marsh development. This feature is usually much larger than the ebb tide delta since the bay is a rela-

tively low energy environment.

Inlets are essential components of the coastal system in terms of estuarine productivity. The periodic influx of salt water maintains the marine character and productivity of these enclosed water bodies. When inlets are closed, the lagoonal water becomes less brackish, and their value as marine systems is gradually lost.

There are two principal differences between

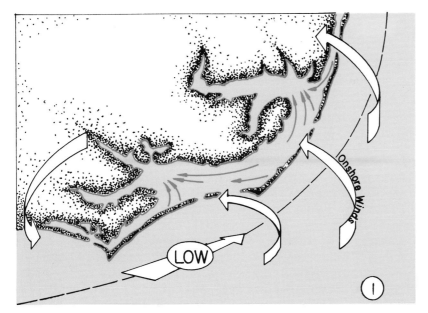
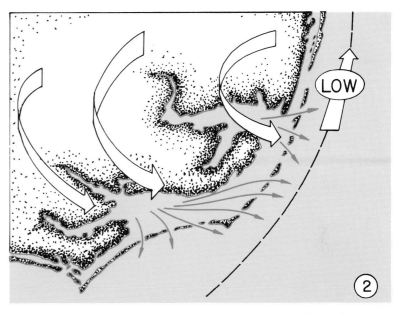

39. Inlets are often created by bayside breaching of a barrier island following the passage of a hurricane.

washover fans and tidal deltas. First, washover fans result from relatively infrequent, storm-related activities, whereas tidal deltas are the product of the twice-daily reversals of the tide. Second, washover fans are built subaerially, whereas tidal deltas develop primarily underwater.

Old inlet sites can be located by the con-spicuous deltaic pattern of salt marshes along the bayshore of coastal barriers. Most islands along the East and Gulf coasts show evidence of previous inlets. In particular, barriers along the Delmarva peninsula and the Outer Banks of North Carolina have typical inlet features along most of their length. The largest inlet features are found along the Texas shoreline from Matagorda Peninsula to Padre Island.

Along the sea island coast of South Carolina, Georgia, and north Florida, inlets are generally associated with large river systems. These sea island type barriers have a Pleistocene origin (see Figure 18). Inlets have been prominent for thousands of years in these areas, and the bays are marsh-filled. Therefore, the typical deltaic patterns of flood tidal deltas are not present.

Lagoons

Lagoons or bays are large bodies of open water that are protected from oceanic forces by coastal barriers; fresh water input is usually limited to land surface runoff. An estuary, however, is a river that empties fresh water into a semi-enclosed basin connected to the sea, resulting in a salinity gradient from full sea strength at the mouth of the estuary to fresh water near the head. Wave action is less significant in these enclosed water bodies than on the ocean beach, and the primary influences on backbarrier sediments are the rise and fall of the tides and activities of organisms.

Sediments generally range from coarse near inlets where tidal currents are strongest to fine at a distance from the inlets. As fine-grained sediment is deposited in the lagoon, mudflats form and eventually become exposed at low tide. The general pattern of particle-size distribution in backbarrier sediments is from fine-grained in shallow water to coarse-grained in deeper water. This distinctive pattern is the opposite of that found on the ocean beach. The distribution of bottom communities, such as shellfish, depends largely on the type of substrate available.

Lagoonal environments are important sites for marine organisms and are very rich in terms of organic productivity. Many marine species require estuarine or lagoonal habitats to survive since a portion of their life cycles are spent in this habitat. Marshes that fringe a lagoon account for a large portion of the total organic productivity which is usable to marine organisms. In addition to fringing marshes, most brackish water environments also support beds of underwater vegetation--most notably eelgrass (Zostera marina)--and various types of algae, both attached and floating in the water.

During periods of heavy rain the salinity levels in backbarrier bays can become quite low, especially when the tide is ebbing. On the other hand, drought and exceptionally warm periods (causing increased evaporation) can lead to high salinities in the lagoon, often very close to normal sea water or supersaline water as in the south Texas bays. Lagoons and bays are shallow and easily mixed by waves, and thus are not stratified by temperature and salinity as are estuaries in river drainage basins.

Barrier Evolution

The long-term behavior of a barrier island depends principally upon the rate of sea level rise, sand supply, and sea energy (Figure 40). Human intervention can also be an important factor when modern technology is applied. Sand supply is often the key to a barrier island's evolution. With a relatively constant supply of sediment, the island can maintain itself in place and build upward with sea level rise (Figure 41). With an excess sand supply, the barrier can actually accrete seaward.

As the Ice Age glaciers melted about 15,000 years ago and sea level rose (see Figure 50), the river valleys were flooded and much of the riverine sediments were trapped in coastal estuaries instead of reaching barrier shorelines. With no new sediment or sediment loss, a barrier island must retreat landward up the coastal plain in order to maintain a constant elevation and prevent submergence (drowning) with sea level rise (Figure 42). In this fashion barriers gain higher positions on the slope of the continental shelf and so maintain a constant elevation relative to the water level, rather than being inundated by the rising sea. Sand from the ocean side of the barrier is transported by water and wind toward the backside of the island so that the whole landform gradually changes its location.

Since the Atlantic and Gulf coastal plain is a broad, gentle sloping surface, a small rise in sea level results in a dramatic horizontal retreat of the land. For a given rise in sea level, a barrier

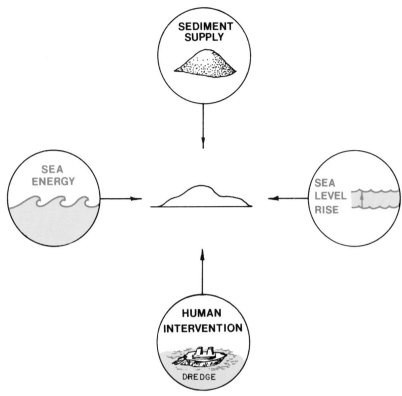

40. Principal factors affecting barrier migration.

island must migrate landward a distance of two or three orders of magnitude of this value (vertical rise) as shown in Figure 42. Along the U.S. East and Gulf coasts, the relative rise has averaged about one foot per century, which corresponds to a horizontal retreat of 100 to 1000 feet per century. In fact, historical shoreline movement studies have shown that many Atlantic coast barrier beaches are eroding 2 to 3 feet per year (200-300 feet per century). Rates of beach erosion along the Louisiana coast are reported at 30+ feet per year

during historic times.

Along the U.S. Northeast coast, there is actually little coastal plain. For example, Nauset Spit is backed by shallow, narrow bays and high relief uplands. Therefore, the landward migration of Nauset Spit in response to sea level rise is resulting in the progressive infilling and shrinking of the enclosed bays (Figure 43). Eventually, the bays will be completely pinched off as the barrier coalesces with the mainland. The true barrier structure will be lost as its sediment is welded onto the mainland shore to form a sandy beach. Under present conditions this eventuality will occur within the next several millennia.

Along the U.S. coastal plain, barriers are migrating landward over the long term as sea level rises. Most people call this erosion, but it is more accurate to speak of retreat when barrier

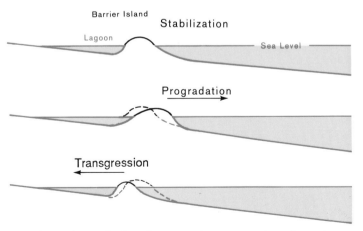

41. A barrier island may (1) remain in place, (2) prograde seaward, or (3) retreat, depending on sediment supply, sea level, and energy conditions.

systems are involved, since these structures are capable of migration as ecological units. Unlike mainland sea cliffs which erode from fixed positions, barriers actually move backward (landward) onto marsh and lagoonal deposits. Indeed, barrier islands have been migrating landward since their creation, which is believed to have occurred approximately 7,000 years ago when the southeast and mid-Atlantic barriers formed on the continental shelf, tens of miles seaward of their present location.

With landward barrier retreat, transported sand buries backbarrier environments, but new marshes develop further landward on the leading edge of the new sediment. Evidence for complete translocation of coastal barriers comes from core samples, which reveal marsh peat underneath the dunes. Salt marsh peat is also frequently exposed at low tide on the ocean beach of retreating barriers (Figure 44), providing further proof that the barrier has migrated over old marshes. This pattern of barrier rollover by overwash after considerable shoreline recession is illustrated by

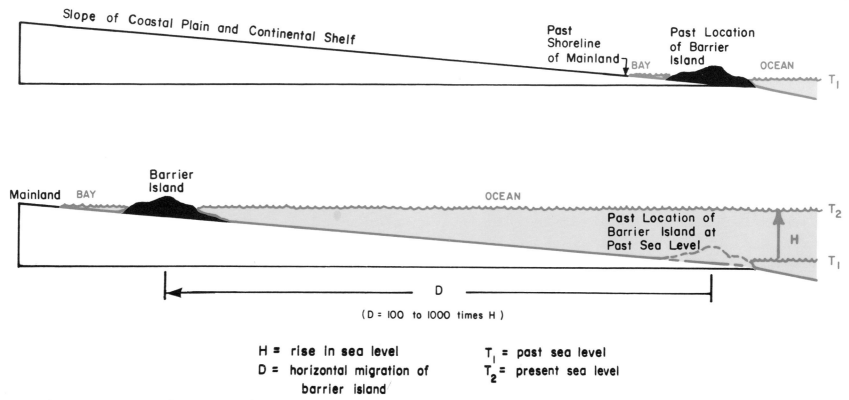

H = rise in sea level
D = horizontal migration of barrier island

T_1 = past sea level
T_2 = present sea level

42. With sea level rise a barrier must retreat up the gradually sloping coastal plain over geologic time. Without migration the barrier can be drowned.

Figure 45. In some cases, stumps from earlier maritime forests are exhumed on the beach foreshore after a major storm (Figure 46).

While some barriers, such as Nauset Spit, Massachusetts, are naturally migrating landward

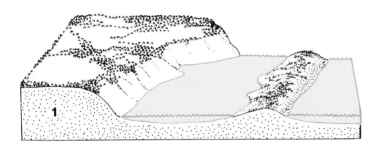
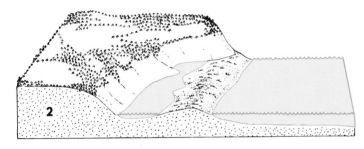
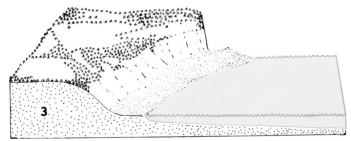

43. Landward migration of Nauset Spit, resulting in the infilling and shrinking of enclosed bays and eventual welding upon the mainland as a sandy beach with barrier demise.

quite rapidly over the short term, others are not. Geomorphic data and quantitative historical map analysis showed that the western end of Fire Island, New York, has remained essentially static in its centroid position for quite a long period of time (up to a millennia). Instead of migrating, this barrier has experienced both ocean and bayside erosion as well as bayside submergence during this

44. Salt marsh peat outcropping on beach foreshore at Assateague Island, Maryland.

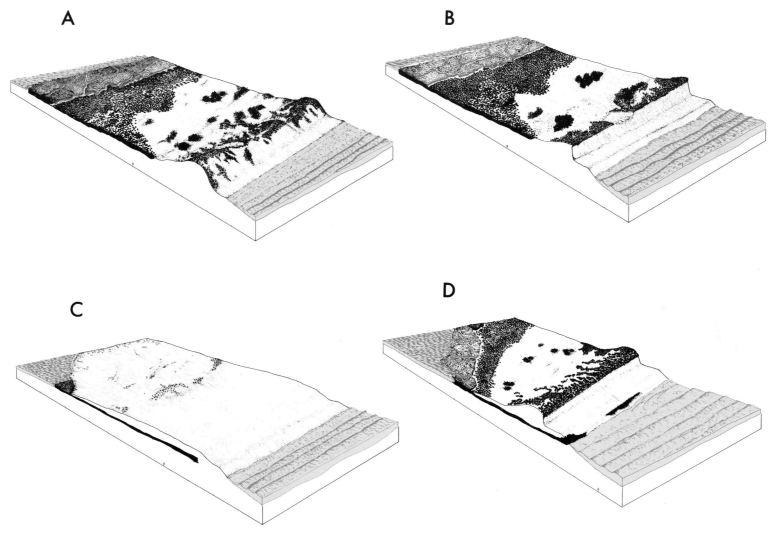

45. Rollover model, illustrating the mechanics of landward retreat which result in the eventual outcropping of salt marsh peat on the beach foreshore.

46.   Tree stumps are exposed in the swash zone at Currituck Spit, Virginia.

time frame (Figure 47).   Hatteras Island, North Carolina has also followed the same trend during recorded times.   Previous studies at Assateague Island, Maryland, showed that barriers must narrow to some critical width before initiation of migration (Figure 48).

Landward migration occurs in response to rising sea level and is achieved during storm conditions by inlet dynamics and overwash processes.   Depending upon wind regime, dune migration may play a role in barrier dynamics.   The mechanisms of sand transport on coastal barriers are shown in Figure 49.   Inlets are a major means of barrier island retreat.   Where a barrier becomes narrow, a new inlet is likely to form during a severe storm, and large quantities of sand will be carried through this breach into the bay.   When an inlet is finally choked with sand and closes, new marshes form on the flood tidal deltas (see Figure 56).   The net result of inlet dynamics is landward migration of the barrier system.

Barriers which are undergoing active retreat actually "roll-over" themselves into the lagoon or bay behind (Figure 45).   The most common mechanism is dune breaching by a severe storm surge which carries beach and dune sand onto the backdune region as overwash.   Sand is deposited between and behind the dunes, and onto marshes or into a lagoon, depending upon storm magnitude and island width.

The frequency of overwash depends on the rate of dune building, storm frequency, and tidal range. Following an overwash, wind begins winnowing new deposits to form dunes.   Prevailing winds tend to blow unstabilized sand off a washover fan toward the ocean or into newly developing dunes.   Dunes grow only to be knocked down and pushed back by the next overwash event on rapidly retreating barriers. Where there are well developed frontal dunes, barriers are subject to overwash only during severe storms that arrive near the high tide period.

Wind-driven dunes are also a factor in the retreat of some barriers, especially if the islands

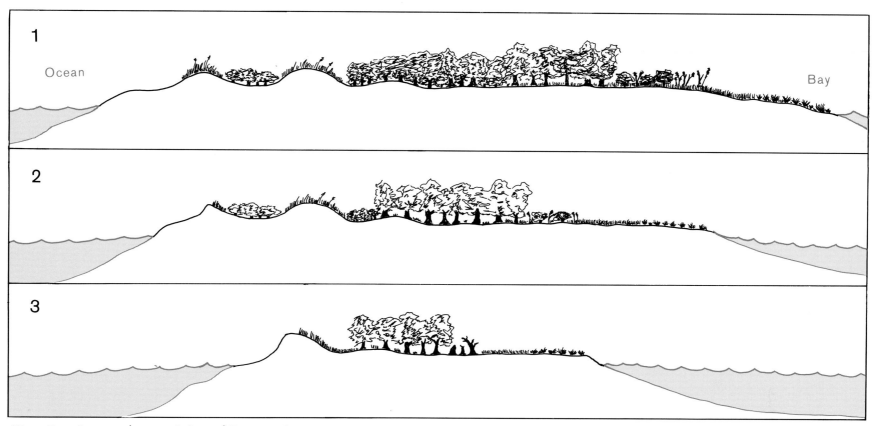

47. Beach erosion and bayside erosion and submergence are the probable response of wide islands to rapid sea level rise.

are oriented across prevailing winds. In some cases, migrating dunes can cover existing marshes and move into the adjacent bay. Human disturbance has resulted in or accelerated the rate of dune migration on many coastal barriers, such as the Province Lands of Cape Cod and Currituck Spit, North Carolina.

The various mechanisms of migration (primarily inlets and overwash) result in sand being pushed landward and upward over older, backbarrier environments, continually raising the base level of the barrier. This process has the effect of maintaining shallow water conditions in the adjacent bay even as sea level rises. If the retreat is too fast, excessive filling of the enclosed lagoon and rapid destruction of the marshes will result. Most barriers will not be submerged as long as retreat

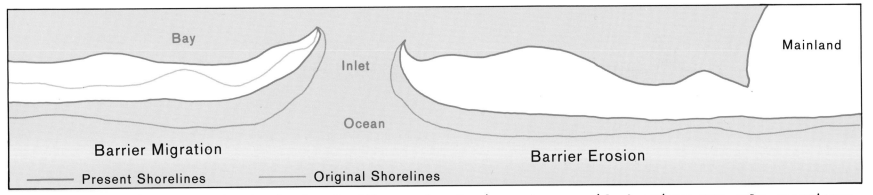

Bay

Inlet

Ocean

Mainland

Barrier Migration

Barrier Erosion

———— Present Shorelines ———— Original Shorelines

48. Narrow barriers can migrate landward with sea level rise, whereas wide barriers may only experience seaside erosion until critical barrier width is achieved.

is possible; the Louisiana barriers are an exception to the rule. Here the land surface is rapidly subsiding so barrier sands are sinking below the surf zone and are permanently lost to the shore.

All of the sand transport processes have been involved in varying degrees in the creation, maintenance, and migration of barrier systems. Most present-day islands have moved a considerable distance since their initial formation, particularly those barriers along the Outer Banks of North Carolina. On the other hand, sea islands such as Cumberland and Sapelo Islands, Georgia, have changed little for thousands of years. It is clear that barrier islands are still evolving and moving in response to oceanic forces, and it is likely that change will occur more rapidly in the future as sea levels continue to rise at accelerated rates.

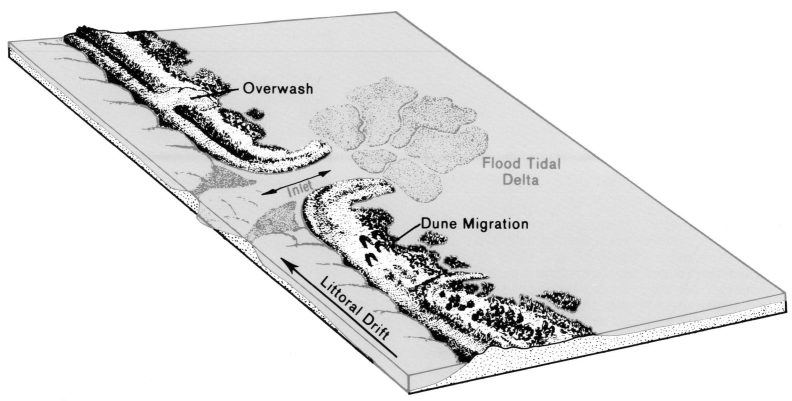

Overwash

Flood Tidal
Delta

Inlet

Dune Migration

Littoral Drift

49. Mechanisms for landward sediment transfer.

Sea Level Rise

Rising sea level is the primary driving force for landward movement of the shoreline. Beach erosion has been theoretically linked to sea level rise (Bruun Rule), and this relationship has been validated by both laboratory wave tank and field experimentation.

Through geological time, sea level has always been rising or falling relative to the land surface. The last major change in sea level occurred during the most recent Ice Age, when sea level was approximately 300 feet lower than present. The volume of water in the sea increased very rapidly after ice melt intensified about 15,000 years ago, with sea level rising at a faster rate than the previous 5,000 years (Figure 50). Presently, the rate of sea level rise, relative to land, averages a foot per century along the mid-Atlantic coast based on tide gauge records (Figure 51).

Where the land is also subsiding, relative sea level rise has been much greater. Recent figures for Charleston, South Carolina, show a rise of nearly fourteen inches since 1920 (Figure 51). Land subsidence is an even more serious problem along the Gulf Coast due to withdrawal of fluids, both groundwater and petroleum. For example, land near Baytown, Texas, has sunk over nine feet in less than 100 years, requiring the installment of dikes to hold back the saline waters of Galveston Bay during ordinary tides.

Local changes in land surface with respect to

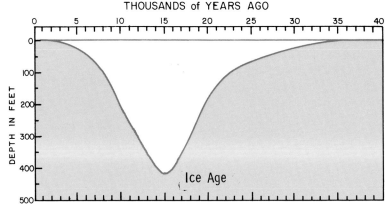

50. Sea Level Rise Curve (from Milliman and Emery, 1968).

sea level are termed isostatic. In northern latitudes, the land surface has been rebounding upward since retreat of the great ice sheets that covered and depressed the land surface. In parts of eastern Canada, the land is actually rising out of the sea since isostatic rebound is greater than eustatic (worldwide) sea level rise. Coastal accretion, rather than erosion, has occurred, and old beach ridges can be found far inland.

While melting of the polar ice caps continues to be a major cause of rising sea level, the rate of rise is expected to accelerate in the future due to increasing global temperatures, driven by higher levels of carbon dioxide in the atmosphere. Due to the greenhouse effect, higher average global temperatures could result in as much as a four to five foot rise within the next 100 years, which would be catastrophic for major cities located in low-lying coastal areas.

All evidence suggests that sea level will

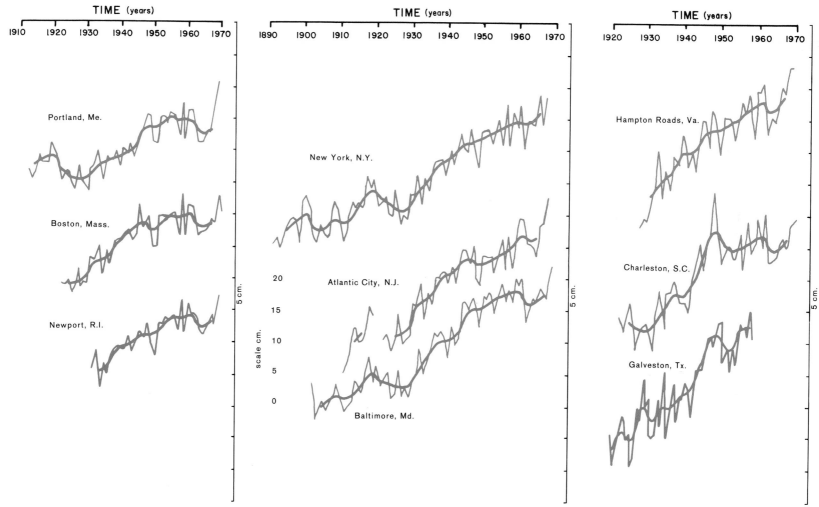

51. Recent sea level changes along the U.S. East and Gulf coasts (from Hicks, 1972).

continue to rise, and in fact, it appears likely that the rise will accelerate. The present upward trend in sea level can neither be ignored nor expected to reverse in the foreseeable future. Indeed, land use planning and engineering practices cannot be predicated on the assumption that sea level will stabilize. It is advisable to consider the "worse case scenario" near an eroding shoreline. Increased flooding and damage during coastal storms can be expected in the future as the beaches and barrier dunes continue to erode, reducing the buffer between human development and the high-energy surf.

Storms

Sea level rise by itself would not be sufficient to drive the barrier system landward. The major amount of sand transport occurs in a quantum fashion during extreme events. Storms that affect the U.S. coastline fall into two basic categories: northeasters and hurricanes. Northeasters (or nor'easters) are so named since the strongest winds frequently come from the northeast. These winter storms originate in the mid-latitudes of the U.S., frequently moving offshore at Cape Hatteras, North Carolina. Building intensity along the coast, they often move northeastward toward New England. Some of the most intense storms and greatest coastal damage along the U.S. East coast have occurred during these nor'easters (such as the February 6-7, 1978 blizzard). The frequency of northeasters is very high, and almost every year several coastal storms of this type affect the shoreline.

One of the most severe storms ever to strike the mid-Atlantic coast occurred on March 5-8, 1962, a result of two low pressure cells converging to form a storm system which extended from Cape Hatteras to Cape Cod. This storm was especially devastating for the following reasons: it occurred during spring high tides; strong northeast winds pushed water onshore, generating a large storm surge for five successive high tides; waves (up to 30 feet high offshore) breached the dunes, subjecting barrier islands to flooding, massive overwashing, and inlet breaching along much of the shoreline (Figure 52).

52. Breaching of Delaware barriers during the March 1962 northeaster.

Hurricanes affect the East and Gulf coasts in the late summer and early fall with September being the most active month. Hurricanes that strike the U.S. coastline are born in the tropical and subtropical latitudes. Beginning as low pressure cells, these small tropical cyclones increase in size and intensity until becoming full-fledged hurricanes (defined as maintaining wind speeds in excess of 74 miles per hour). These storms move forward into the Gulf of Mexico or turn northeastward toward the eastern seaboard.

Near the center of a hurricane, winds may gust to more than 200 miles per hour. While intense winds are the most obvious threat to life and property and do much damage, massive storm surges are by far the greatest cause of deaths and destruction on coastal barriers. Six thousand people died on Galveston Island, Texas, during the hurricane of 1900, which still stands as the worst natural disaster in U.S. history.

A storm surge is a super-elevated mound of water that accompanies a hurricane as it passes the coast or makes landfall. Surge and hurricane-driven waves act in deadly combination to hammer the shore, sweeping across low-lying coastal areas. Barrier islands are forced to absorb the storm brunt, reducing the force of wind and wave before they reach the mainland. This explains why these landforms are called "barriers". During the infamous Hurricane Camille in 1969, a 22-foot storm surge inundated Pass Christian, Mississippi, and the hurricane waves destroyed the beachfront development.

Storms are an integral part of the oceanic environment, and records since the 1500s show that hurricanes have affected the U.S. coastline throughout historic time. All portions of the Gulf and East coasts have been affected by coastal storms. There is an indication that hurricanes come in cycles. The last series of major storms along the U.S. Atlantic coast occurred during the 1950s. During the past three decades, most hurricanes have entered the Gulf of Mexico rather than travelling up the East coast. The great Atlantic hurricanes will return in the future. Unfortunately, most of the barrier construction has occurred during this unusually calm period.

Sand movement along a beach is accomplished by longshore currents. As waves approach a beach at an angle, a current is generated along the shore, resulting in sand movement in this direction. In general, the average direction along the U.S. East coast is from north to south, although there are many variations.

Barriers can form as sand is transported from a source, such as an eroding glacial headland, for deposition into open water. The alongshore transport of sediment by wave action tends to lengthen the beach in the direction that waves generally strike a coastline. These currents flow parallel to shore, and therefore tend to build relatively straight sediment deposits along the coast, even if the shoreline is indented to form a bay (Figure 53). By this mechanism a barrier spit can develop in areas that were previously open water within a few decades. Only an adequate, uninterrupted longshore supply of sand from the source area will guarantee the continued growth and existence of the spit.

The early stages of spit growth are dominated by overwash that moves sand across the barrier. At the same time, tidal currents move huge quantities of sediment (gravels, sands, silts, and clays) around the end of an accreting spit. This material is deposited in the quiet waters (the developing bay) in the lee of the protective barrier. Spartina grasses colonize the backbarrier sediments, and the marsh continues to expand with the growing spit. Redfield showed that Sandy

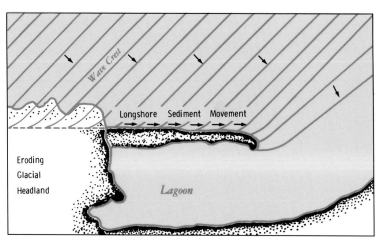

53. Spit formation along a coastline by oblique wave approach and resulting littoral drift.

Neck, Massachusetts, developed principally by this process (Figure 54). The protective spit allowed for the progressive growth of the enclosed Barnstable salt marsh.

Spit formation through the mechanism of longshore sediment transport is the principal process shaping barriers. Rates of littoral drift average 200,000-300,000 cubic yards per year along the mid-Atlantic coast.

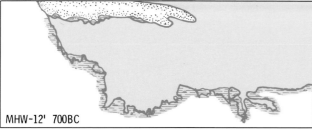

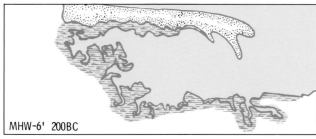

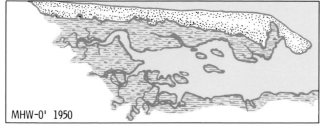

MHW-18' 1300BC

MHW-12' 700BC

MHW-6' 200BC

MHW-0' 1950

0   6000
Feet

54. Reconstruction of the growth of Sandy Neck and development of Barnstable Marsh, Cape Cod, Massachusetts (from Redfield, 1972).

Inlets are important for barrier island migration by developing flood tidal deltas (Figure 55). A portion of sediment moving along a coast is swept through an inlet and into a lagoon by the flood currents. Since bay water is less turbulent than that along the ocean shore, sand settles out to form a tidal delta. Some sediment is moved back out to sea as the current reverses on the ebb tide, but usually the net change results in bay sediment deposition. The growth rate of a flood tidal delta is a measure of the amount of sand being trapped from the littoral drift by the inlet.

Flood tidal deltas serve as platforms upon which salt marshes can develop once an inlet closes or migrates downdrift (Figure 56). The majority of salt marshes behind barrier systems along the U.S. East coast originally developed on old tidal deltas. The conspicuous deltaic pattern of the marshes and the presence of sandy materials underneath the salt marsh peat are good evidence for such an origin. For example, the Outer Banks of North Carolina have been much affected by inlets during historic times (Figure 57), and most of the backbarrier marshes have formed in this matter.

There is evidence that a cycle of inlet formation, marsh development, and overwash occurs on most barrier islands as they migrate landward. An inlet will occur at a narrow point along a barrier, then migrate downdrift until it closes or reaches the end of the spit (Figure 58). With time, the barrier will migrate over older inlet or overwash

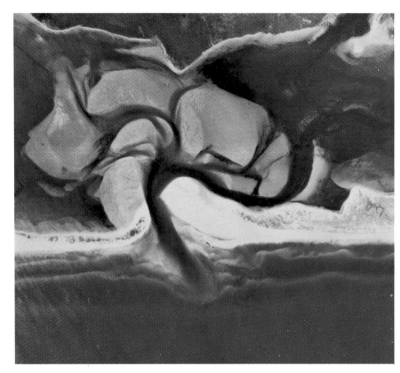

55. This tidal inlet in the southern Gulf of St. Lawrence displays an extensive lobe of the flood tidal delta, a distinctive inlet channel and poorly developed ebb tidal delta.

deposits. While the inlet is migrating downdrift along the barrier, earlier sediments and marsh peat will be eroded. At the same time, new sediments will be deposited behind the updrift section of the inlet, allowing for the development of new marshes (Figure 59).

The depth of salt marsh peat on old tidal deltas behind coastal barriers is generally shallow

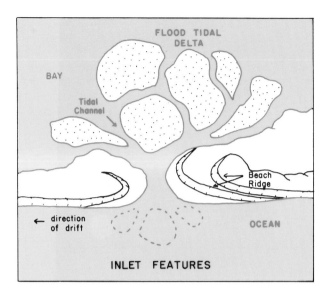

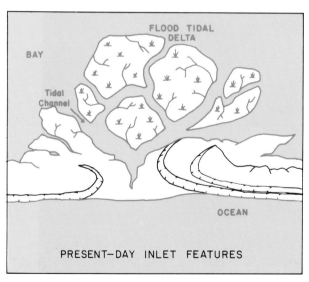

56. Development of extensive salt marshes on a flood tidal delta, following inlet closure.

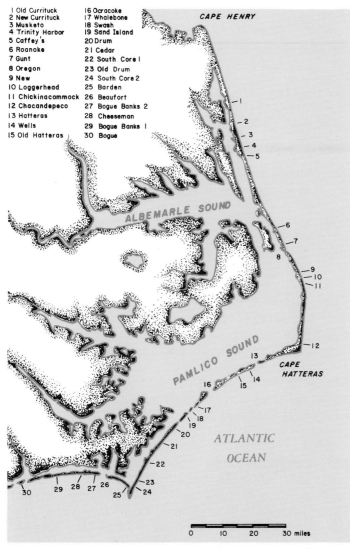

57. Location of historical inlets along the Outer Banks of North Carolina (from Fisher).

(less than a few feet), suggesting that these marshes are young. Along most barrier systems, outcrops of salt marsh peat can be found on the lower foreshore, particularly after a major storm (see Figure 44). This is further evidence that barriers are continuously changing position by migrating landward ahead of the rising sea.

A model for rapidly migrating barrier islands has been derived from the coupling of field and historical aerial photographic studies. The best example is the northern end of Assateague Island, Maryland, which has been eroding at the rate of 30 to 40 feet per year since the stabilization of Ocean City Inlet in 1935 (see Figure 84). This dramatic shoreline recession should not be considered as natural, but permits an evaluation of the relative effectiveness of inlet dynamics and overwash processes in terms of island migration.

Landward displacement of a barrier ecosystem seems to depend largely upon inlet dynamics (Figure 60). Temporary and migrating permanent inlets provide the bases -- that is, the large flood tidal deltas upon which the island environments are established. These substrates serve as platforms for marsh development and hence landward extension of the bay shoreline. Subsequently, wind-blown and overwash sediments can be deposited on top of this accretionary base. These latter two forms of sediment movement are responsible for the vertical growth of a barrier island.

Overwash becomes an effective transport mechanism for island migration only where the barrier width is less than a critical value (400 to 700 feet at Assateague Island). Inlet breaching and subsequent flood tidal delta formation is viewed as the only mechanism by which the island can exceed

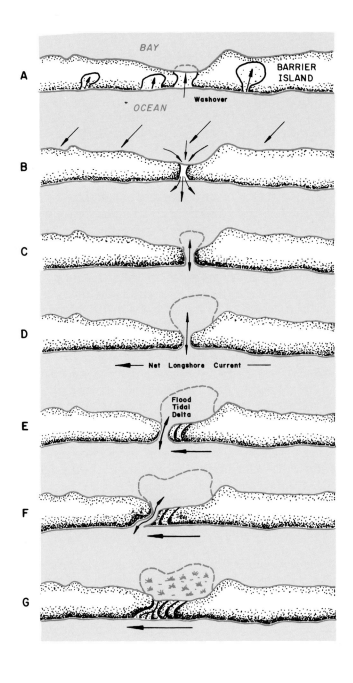

58. Sequential diagrams illustrate the process of inlet breaching, migration, closing and development of large flood tidal delta.

(A) Initiation of storm causes wave overwashing of barrier island at low places in dune lines.

(B) Flow of superelevated water in the bay, driven by the strong (northwest) offshore winds near the end of the storm, results in the creation of an inlet at low, narrow points along the island.

(C) Normal tidal currents through the inlet throat, with change in tide, result in the creation and initial growth of large flood tidal delta in the bay.

(D) The flood tidal delta continues to grow as sediment accumulates in the bay. The ebb tidal delta on the ocean side is also present, but not prominent, due to disturbance by ocean waves.

(E) Net longshore currents to the south result in migration of the inlet southward, resulting in the increased size and growth of the flood tidal delta.

(F) Eventually the water path through the inlet throat area becomes so long and tortuous that the inlet's efficiency is greatly reduced.

(G) The flushing of sediment from the inlet throat by tidal currents is overpowered by the deposition of sand in the throat caused by the longshore current, and the inlet closes. The new sediment on the bayside (flood tidal delta) provides an ideal substrate for marsh growth and the island has been effectively widened at this point by the process of inlet dynamics.

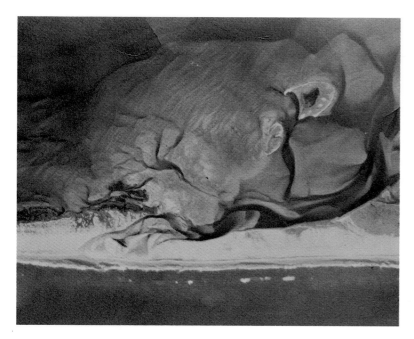

59. Drum Inlet, North Carolina is shown shortly
after closure. Note that the net littoral
drift is from right to left as indicated by
the now closed, meandering inlet channel.

the 700 foot width limitation along an eroding
shoreline. Thus the lateral growth of a transgressive barrier is controlled largely by inlet
dynamics, but the vertical accumulation of sediments
is governed by the interaction between overwash-
aeolian processes and plant communities. Where
shoreline erosion is rapid and overwash is frequent
and severe, colonization by stabilizing beach
grasses is prevented. Without dune establishment,
the island remains barren and low as it migrates
landward (Figure 60).

The second principal method by which sediment
is transported across barrier islands is overwash.
This occurs when storm waves breach the barrier
dunes and push beach sand across the island.
Overwash is the means by which barrier flats are
created and sand is deposited above the normal
high tide mark.

With the advent of a major storm, overwash
may appear to be catastrophic as the barrier
environments are severely stressed by this natural
event (Figure 61). However, viewed over the longer
term (hundreds of years), overwash can be viewed as
a nearly continuous process, shaping and reshaping
the barrier. In the conduct of this overall
process, the barrier is displaced landward.

Transgressive barrier islands are position-
ally unstable so that no area remains intact in-
definitely, but the same environmental conditions
and habitats are continually recreated so that
plant colonization and revegetation can yield the
same plant communities through time. In this
manner, the barrier renews itself periodically,
plant species are held principally at the grass
stage, and ecological succession is precluded.

Overwash frequency depends on barrier exposure
and orientation, frequency of major storms, wave
energy, tidal range, and dune dimensions. Therefore, the extent of overwash activity varies
regionally. Where tide ranges are low (microtidal) and storm frequency high, such as along the

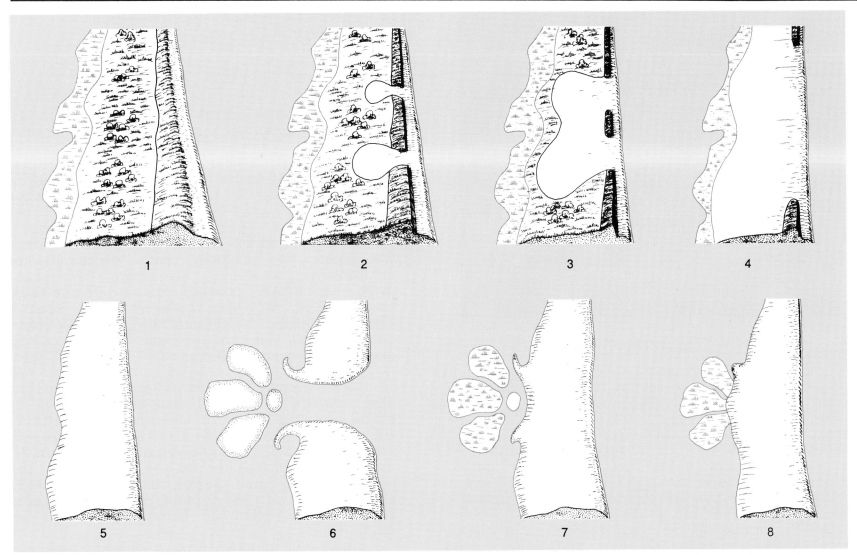

60. Model of barrier island dynamics for a rapidly eroding shoreline. Note the progression in intensity and dominance of overwash with time. Opening of a temporary inlet greatly increases the barrier's width. The barrier is kept low and largely barren by the frequent and severe overwash surges.

61. Nauset Beach-Eastham, Cape Cod, Massachusetts, was extensively overwashed during the
February 6-7, 1978 northeaster.

Outer Banks of North Carolina, overwash is a regular
event without naturally high or artificially-stabil-
ized dunes.   Conversely, where tide ranges are
large (mesotidal) such as at Nauset Spit,
Massachusetts, the chance that a storm will arrive
at the highest tide levels and overtop the barrier

is considerably less, and hence overwash is an
infrequent event.

Overwash at Cape Lookout, North Carolina, is
also encouraged by sea oats (Uniola paniculata) type
vegetation (generally resulting in discontinuous
dune lines). This cuspate foreland is in the
path of major storms, including both tropical
(hurricanes) and extratropical (winter northeasters)
storms.   There is apparently little new sediment
being introduced to the system, and it appears that
Core Banks is feeding on its own sand supplies in
the migrational process. The cumulative result of
these conditions is expressed in barrier morphology-
-Core Banks remains in a low profile state,
experiencing frequent and often severe overwash.
By contrast, the U.S. Northeast coast has a much
larger tidal range and vigorous dune-building
vegetation (Ammophila, American beach grass), which
limits overwash frequency.   The most extensively
overwashed regions of the East Coast tend to be the
Delmarva peninsula and the Outer Banks of North
Carolina.   Major washover features can also be
found along the Gulf coast, particularly the Texas
barrier islands.

Barrier migration by the overwash process is
most apparent when large lengths of an island are
overtopped.   Sand is moved into the bay, and thus
the landward limit of the barrier is visibly
extended (Figure 61). Overwash sediments, however,
are usually deposited on top of the living salt
marsh (Figure 62), which develop on ancient flood
tidal deltas.

The ecological response to overwash is different on U.S. Northern and Southern barrier
islands.   Godfrey showed that Southern barrier
flat communities dominated by Spartina patens are

able to recover to initial biomass levels within a few years following overwash. In contrast, salt marsh vegetation on Northern barriers dies when buried by significant overwash deposits. Recolonization of washovers occurs principally by drift line species. Therefore after a major overwash, dune environments replace the salt marsh community in the North. This difference in ecological response may partly account for the fact that many Southern barriers are broad and flat and dominated by overwash-adapted grasslands, whereas Northern barriers are characterized by dune environments.

A generalized model of vegetative response and barrier retreat by overwash along the U.S. Northeast coast is illustrated by Figure 63. These barrier systems tend to be dominated by dune ridges and overall dune topography. American beach grass

62. Overwash sediments deposited as a fan on top of the living salt marsh at North Beach, Cape Cod, Massachusetts.

(_Ammophila_ _breviligulata_), the dominant dune stabilizer, produces extensive, dense grasslands. Thus a typical profile exhibits a high, fairly continuous, but often scarped, dune ridge, fronted by a narrow beach face and backed by a second dune zone or field. The dunes grade into an intertidal salt meadow cordgrass marsh (_Spartina_ _patens_) with little extent of barrier flats (Fig. 63A).

Along an eroding shoreline, the barrier dune continues to narrow through time as seaward erosion exceeds backdune accretion (Fig. 63B). Finally, storm waves and accompanying surges result in dune breaching and creation of massive washovers (Fig. 63C). Landward-flanking salt marshes are buried and killed by deep overwash deposits. Where sand reaches the bayshore, a new substrate for salt marsh development is created. Drift piles serve as nuclei for the formation of new dune fields, which are initially established toward the bayward edge of large washovers (Fig. 63D). Prevailing winds redistribute the loose overwash sand and live plants grow vertically through the accumulating sand (Fig. 63E). This biogeological process can result in upward growth rates of dunes exceeding three feet per year under optimal conditions of plentiful sand supply. Eventually, a new, high foredune is created, backed by extensive dune fields with intervening low areas. Complete recovery of a washover occurs when the frontal edge of the new dune merges with adjacent backdunes and the barrier profile is increased above the overwash threshold (Fig. 63F). Through the culmination of these processes, the subaerial barrier environments have been effectively displaced landward in a quantum fashion.

Overwash has contributed to the migrational process, largely by making available fresh sand

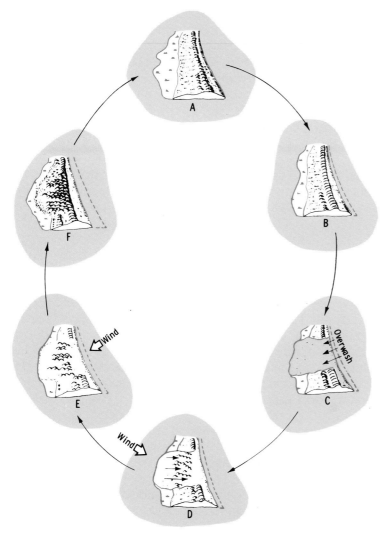

63. Model of ecological response to overwash on a retreating U.S. Northeast barrier.

for dune development (vertical growth) and to a lesser degree by adding new sediment to the bay-shore (lateral expansion). It is in this fashion that high areas (dunes) become low areas (wash-overs) in a cyclic fashion. Therefore, the spatial occurrence of overwash has the effect of displacing the barrier landward, and different sections of the barrier represent various stages in this cyclic phenomenon.

Overwash, however, is not the dominant process by which most barriers move landward since the amount of sediment transported by this means is usually too small. Inlet formation, when tidal currents cut a channel below sea level, moves far greater quantities of sediment into a lagoon over the long term and is the major process for barrier migration. Tidal deltas associated with inlets provide the sediment on which extensive marshes can develop. However, overwash and aeolian processes control the vertical growth of the migrating barrier island.

Dune Migration

Direct movement of sand by wind is the final mechanism of transport on coastal barriers (Figure 64). Aeolian transport results in the formation of dunes wherever sand can be moved from a beach or washover fan into an area that contains either vegetation or fences to anchor the sand. Any

64. A 35-40 mph northwest (offshore) wind at the northern end of Assateague Island, Maryland, is moving considerable quantities of sand from the dunes to the beach.

resistance to air flow leads to the deposition of sand around that structure. Grasses play an important role in the process of forming dunes by serving as a baffle to the flow and by growing upward and outward through the accumulating sand.

Dune migration is a principal means of landward sediment transport along some barriers. At Sandy Neck on Cape Cod Bay, Massachusetts, large dunes are migrating onto Barnstable salt marsh. It is not clear whether human habitation and past misuse initiated this process, but vegetation destruction by off-road vehicles has accelerated the rate of migration. On portions of Cumberland Island, Georgia, large dunes are also migrating across salt marshes and burying maritime forests (Figure 65).

Dunes can remain stabilized by vegetation for centuries if not disrupted by human activities, as in the case of the Province Lands of Cape Cod, Massachusetts. The original dune systems were covered by a dense and highly developed climax forest of beech, oak and maple. However, the vegetation was eliminated with the arrival of Europeans around 1620 from their need for wood and grazing land. Once this protective cover was destroyed, prevailing winds began moving sand into previously stabilized areas of vegetation. The migrating dunes buried forests, ponds, and bogs. Ghost forests of dead trees and stumps are left in the wake of this man-induced dune migration.

Overwash and dune processes work together to move sediment landward at Padre Island, Texas. During hurricanes, gaps in the barrier dune line are opened and overwash sediments are deposited on the barrier flats. Large quantities of sand are blown from the beach through the dune gap onto the

65. Dune migration on Cumberland Island, Georgia.

washover fan by the prevailing easterly winds
(Figures 66 and 67). A large, migrating dune
quickly develops. Vegetative growth finally entraps
enough sediment to close the dune breach. The sand
source is thus cut off, but these large (25 to 50
foot) dunes continue to move landward across the
landscape.

66. Dune repair is nearly complete, but the dune form continues to migrate landward across Padre Island, Texas.

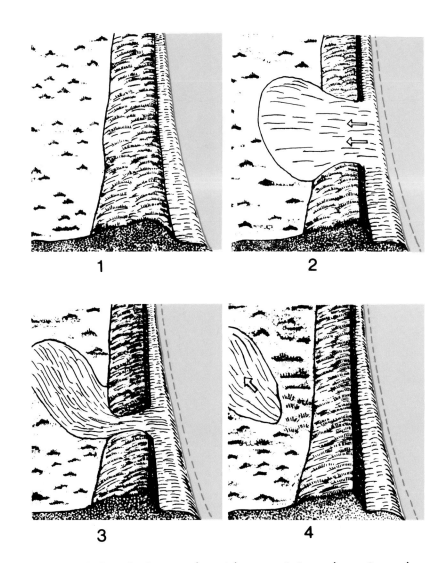

1   2

3   4

67. Model of dune migration and barrier dynamics for Padre Island, Texas (from Mathewson et al., 1975).

Recreational Impacts

Sandy Beaches

Foredunes and Backdunes

Salt Marshes and Tidal Flats

During the past few decades, recreational pressures on coastal ecosystems have greatly increased. The impacts can be grouped into two basic categories: pedestrian trampling and off-road vehicle (ORV) traffic. The amount of impact depends on the type of use and the susceptibility of the system being affected. Each natural system has its own level of tolerance, and this sensitivity must be determined in order to devise management strategies for alleviating or minimizing impacts.

Coastal ecosystems are well adapted to severe environmental conditions and are not fragile in the usual sense. Natural stresses include large variations in temperature, salinity, moisture, burial by sand, and salt water flooding. These ecosystems are fragile only in the sense that the new stresses being applied by modern, mobile people are too severe. For instance, plants did not evolve with vehicular stresses and therefore are not adapted to this impact.

The greatest difficulties occur in the National Parks, where two goals are sought: recreational use of the resources and preservation of these same resources. This basic conflict becomes increasingly difficult to resolve as more and more people flock to the coasts.

The beach is an important site for nutrient recycling, drift-line deposition, and development of new sand dunes. It also serves as a habitat for some animals, including invertebrates and nesting shorebirds. Vehicular usage of this zone can be quite high, particularly during the summer vacation season.

On some beach stretches the most characteristic trait of the backshore is massive, washboard ruts (Figure 68). Vehicle passage increases surface roughness, which can lead to greater beach variability and increased sand movement. Vehicular passage also breaks the (salt) crust, which can initiate sand movement by the wind. With an off-shore wind, this sand can be blown toward the ocean and lost to the longshore current system.

The churning of the beach sand by the wheels can have a direct impact on beach biota. Vehicular impacts along the New England coast are less significant because there are fewer organisms. However, southerly beaches have larger populations, greater diversity and larger fauna, such as ghost crabs, that can be directly affected by vehicle passage.

Ghost crabs (Ocypode quadrata) serve as an excellent indicator species for beach invertebrates since they are fairly large in size and quite numerous from New Jersey to Texas. Studies conducted at Assateague Island, Virginia, have determined the relative numbers of ghost crabs at sites

68. The entire beach profile at North Beach, Cape Cod, Massachusetts, is scarred by ORV tracks.

with different recreational usages. The average number of crabs per sample plot (circle with 60 foot radius) taken over a summer season were found to be as follows: 10 per sample on the wild beach, 19 per plot in the pedestrian impact sites, 1 in light ORV, and 0.3 in heavy ORV-usage areas. Pedestrians appear to have no harmful effects on ghost crabs; instead, the crabs may be capitalizing on the food scraps scattered across the beach by bathers.

The two ORV sites studied at Assateague had significantly lower numbers of ghost crabs than those in natural areas. There was also a difference between these two areas, with more traffic resulting in still fewer crabs. ORVs could be interfering with crabs in two ways: (1) by crushing and burying them inside their burrows as vehicles pass overhead, or (2) by interrupting the reproductive cycle. It was also noticed that almost all crabs in ORV-impacted areas were quite small or young; it is quite likely that the life expectancy for crabs in impacted areas is rather short. Vehicular disturbance results in either fewer new crabs or no reproduction at all, with new inhabitants migrating from the undisturbed areas. Ghost crabs are not a commercially important species, but do occupy a midpoint in the food chain, breaking down and digesting beach detritus (decaying organic matter) and serving in turn as food for birds and fish.

The high beach (backshore) is very heavily impacted by vehicles as it is a relatively flat and dry surface. It is here that drift accumulates, sea birds nest, and new dunes form along accreting beaches. Drift, which consists chiefly of organic material deposited on the backshore during high spring tides or storms, is particularly sensitive to impact. In addition, drift may play a role in recycling nutrients back to the sea, and it contains fragments and seeds of dune plants which serve as a significant site for new dune development (Figure 69). Once the plants are established, windborne sand is deposited around clumps of detritus and vegetation to form the embryonic dune. American beachgrass (Ammophila breviligula-ta), a common northern drift line plant, is able to grow through these aeolian deposits to provide a surface against which more sand accumulates.

Thus, new dunes can develop, provided they are not destroyed by storms and ORV traffic.

The shearing and compressional effects of ORV passage extend to a depth of approximately six inches; the shear stresses of the turning wheels disaggregate the drift and break plant rhizomes. The integrity of drift lines, the precursors of new dunes, is destroyed by ORV traffic as the material is scattered about the beach. Vehicle traffic pulverizes and kills seedlings of annuals and the young plants of perennials, such as Ammophila, that are associated with drift. Essentially all drift-line vegetation is killed when driven over by ORVs.

69. A single ORV pass can destroy drift line plants, which are the precursors of new sand dunes (Assateague Island, Virginia).

The beach is also a habitat for shorebirds. Four general types of disturbance by ORVs were noted: (1) flushing of feeding birds; (2) flushing of resting flocks; (3) reduction of the food supply by systematic compaction of tidal flats; and (4) flushing of nesting birds and destruction of nests. The principal studies have been directed at determining the effects of pedestrian and vehicular approach on beach-nesting seabirds, in particular the least tern (Sterna albifrons).

With complete enclosure of nesting areas and wardening, least terns can successfully reproduce on the beach, despite proximate ORV traffic and associated high levels of human disturbance. Enclosures serve as a refuge from human disturbances, act as a barrier to ORVs, and thus help to direct and channelize traffic to peripheral areas. Without this positive management approach, nests and young of beach-nesting seabirds, particularly terns, are highly vulnerable to disruption.

Controlled impacting experiments showed that birds acclimate to vehicles passing close to their nests, but flush when persons or dogs approached. Vehicles can come twice as close to sitting birds before they take flight than people on foot. Free-running pets that enter the colony cause more harm than numerous vehicles passing around the enclosure. When nesting colonies are protected by fences and drivers avoid these areas, ORV impact on birds can be minimal, particularly where beaches are wide.

Where there are nesting sites on narrow beaches, direct confrontations between vehicles and birds are likely to result, and the birds will suffer accordingly. Forced by spring or storm high tides, vehicles travel higher on the beach, and occasionally through colonies and along the

70. During exceptionally high tides, drivers are forced to travel along the face of dune, disrupting nesting seabird colonies. Beaches should be closed to all traffic during these times.

dune toe (Figure 70). In other cases, entry may be of malicious intent, although such events are rare. Recreational impact, such as pedestrian flushing of nesting birds and vehicles running over eggs and chicks, can be minimized by continued posting of nesting colonies and by law enforcement.

The dune zone consists of two basic parts: newly formed foredunes and more mature backdunes. Dunes catch and store sand blown from the beach and are dependent upon vegetation for stability and development. They are the natural barriers against severe storm flooding of backdune habitats. Dune vegetation can be divided into grassland communities, which represent the first stages in dune succession, and woody communities, characteristic of more stabilized dunes.

In the Northeast, the foredunes are dominated by American beach grass (<u>Ammophila</u> <u>breviligulata</u>). Along the southeast Atlantic and Gulf coasts, sea oats (<u>Uniola</u> <u>paniculata</u>) and salt meadow grass (<u>Spartina</u> <u>patens</u>) are the primary dune colonizers. The more stabilized backdunes at Cape Cod that are subject to impact are stabilized by bearberry and <u>Hudsonia</u> heathlands.

The major pedestrian impact on coastal barriers is foredune degradation caused by uncontrolled crossings. Park visitors often opt for the shortest route between their car or campground and the beach. Large numbers of people crossing the dunes have resulted in: (1) dissection of the dune field by the formation of numerous pathways across and along the foredune (Figure 71); (2) development of large, barren areas (blowouts), where dune vegetation has been completely destroyed; and (3) retardation of new dune growth and development.

71. Pedestrian traffic is having an adverse affect on dune topography at Stinson Beach, a barrier spit on the California coast. Pathways have carved the foredune into many separate sections.

Pedestrian trampling first results in the formation of V-shaped notches in the dune crest. When viewed from above, the paths are funnel shaped--narrow at the dune crest and flared at the base. This characteristic shape reflects the usage pattern as people converge to cross the dune line.

With heavy and continued utilization, these initial notches quickly become large breachways

72. Newly developing foredunes at Assateague Island, Virginia, have become laced by a network of pedestrian trails that lead from the beach to the parking lot crossover.

through the foredune (Figure 72). Field surveys at Assateague Island have shown that the loss of elevation in a devegetated pathway can amount to over two feet annually. Complete sections of the barrier dune can be expected to disappear in the near future. These areas can serve as passageways for overwash surges during storms, subjecting the backdune environments to artificially-induced salt-water flooding.

Other studies have shown that dune trampling can result in a reduction in the number of species and biomass (due to devegetation). The steeper the angle of the dune face subjected to pedestrian traffic, the more rapid and long-lasting are the destructive effects on the dune vegetation and morphology. Subsequent blowouts result in dune instability and lowering of dune crest elevations.

A positive management approach of channeling

and controlling pedestrian traffic through the erection of boardwalks is often necessary. Normal traffic at major beach access points easily exceeds the tolerance level of dune plants. Carefully planned wooden walkways can channel any number of people to desired locations over the dunes. Walkways, built in several coastal parks, have proven very successful; such facilities exist at Fire Island and Cape Cod National Seashores. These structures prevent deterioration of a major resource--dune vegetation.

As an alternative to the construction of artificial structures, dune crossovers can be protected by the placement of hard-packed dirt. Since this material is erodable by rain runoff and the wind to some degree, a maintenance program must be scheduled. Where foredune erosion due to natural beach recession is a problem, this approach may be more cost-effective since boardwalk replacement and repair due to winter storms can be quite expensive. In either case, physical constraints such as fences and bushes may be needed to close off illegal crossovers, at least initially, to funnel the pedestrian traffic to controlled access points.

The effects of vehicles on dunes depends upon which portion of the dune is impacted. On Cape Cod where American beachgrass (Ammophila) is expanding directly onto the beach, research showed that fewer than 50 passes can prohibit seaward growth and development of the foredune system. Experimental studies at Fire Island, New York, have shown that only one pass per two weeks can cause a retreat of the vegetation up the dune face. This amount of impact can be caused by a single individual forced to drive along the dune toe during spring tide conditions (Figure 70). The tolerance levels of Ammophila along the U.S. mid-Atlantic and Southeast regions have not yet been experimentally determined. Due to the reduced vigor of Ammophila at this southern extent of its growth range, a greater susceptibility to impact and probably a slower rate of recovery is anticipated.

It is clear that driving along the front of an advancing Ammophila community will effectively stop new growth. Continuous ORV impact along a foredune front can lead to human-induced acceleration of natural erosion and dune scarping. Such traffic will also prevent the healing of erosion scarps by interfering with the natural tendency of Ammophila to invade and colonize open sand.

The effects of experimental ORV impacts on Ammophila vegetation at Cape Cod showed that low levels of impact (few hundred passes) were sufficient to cause maximum damage to the plants. In this sense, Ammophila vegetation does not have a "carrying capacity" for vehicles. Once started, a vehicle track will remain open and bare with only minimal use.

Recolonization proceeds according to the overall vigor of the vegetation. Near the beach and in the foredune where growing conditions are most favorable, complete recovery can occur within four years at Cape Cod. Recovery on backdune areas takes much longer; experimental ORV tracks are still visible after four years. Other studies have shown that ORV tracks in backdune areas are present even after eight years of protection. Thus, ORV effects are longer lasting when further from the source of new sand that promotes optimal growth of Ammophila. Natural regrowth can be easily set back by passage of a few vehicles.

Vehicular passes across the barrier dunes can result in devegetation and blowouts, and these pathways can serve as overwash channels during storm conditions. Observations at Nauset Spit, Cape Cod, indicate that many of the smaller breaches are indeed man-made (Figure 73). In addition, vehicular traffic over existing washovers prevents reestablishment of dune vegetation on these barren regions. Thus, ORV-induced breaches may be accelerating the overwash process, resulting in greater barrier instability and more rapid landward retreat.

ORVs have also resulted in denudation and consequent lowering of portions of the stabilized Province Lands dunes of Cape Cod (Figure 74). The physical forces applied to the sand by climbing and descending wheels result in a downward transport of sand. Over a period of time the profile may be significantly lowered in those areas where

73. Vehicular traffic and subsequent sand deflation by the wind can result in artificial breaches of the foredune (Nauset Spit, Massachusetts.)

numerous vehicles traverse the dune.

In addition to and more important than direct sand displacement, vehicular passage precludes reestablishment of plant communities. These areas remain open to wind erosion and blowouts soon develop, particularly where oriented to face the prevailing winds. The dunes will then become unstable and begin to migrate unless controlled. Many open dune slopes and migrating sands, now very much in evidence throughout the Province Lands, owe their present conditions if not their origin, to the continued use of off-road vehicles, especially the illegal, occasional dunebusters. Unvegetated sand dunes will continue migrating as long as traffic is permitted across crests or steeply-sloping areas.

More stabilized vegetation, such as bearberry and beach heather, are also sensitive to ORV impact. Their rate of recovery is even slower than that of beach grass (Ammophila). After four years of monitoring, ORV tracks in the heathland community were still clearly visible and largely bare. Therefore, the most stable sites, and those with natural stresses such as drought and low nutrient levels, take the longest time to recover.

Designated trails across dune vegetation must be maintained. Because the impact of vehicles is such that the first few hundred passes cause maximum damage, a "minimum number" or "carrying capacity" cannot be achieved in a practical sense. If ORV traffic is necessary, it is important to establish a few well-managed "heavy use" trails than to allow for the development of many "low-use" ones. Since the amount of environmental degradation will be nearly equal for every track, the objective is to limit the number of trails.

Without maintenance, trails can quickly deteriorate dunes to areas subject to washboarding and/or flooding, and drivers will create new trails (Figure 75), effectively widening the impacted area. Dune grass can be transplanted to restore a damaged dune, once it has been closed to all vehicular traffic (see Figure 88).

Wooden ORV ramps should be built and maintained over dune lines to provide beach access through the dune zone. Such ramps are most critical where lowering of the dune line might lead to greater storm hazards for critical habitats or facilities behind the dune. New routes over dunes to the beach should not be allowed without adequate ramps that protect the dune system. Thus, ORV impact can be lessened through structural controls

74. Vehicles caused an alteration of shape and dune truncation (Province Lands of Cape Cod, Massachusetts).

75. Continued ORV traffic keeps the trails devegetated, and wind erosion eventually lowers the elevation of the sand road. During rainy periods or high tides the road floods, and drivers are forced to cut a new, higher dune trail (Nauset Spit, Massachusetts).

or restrictive approaches. In general, however, off-road vehicle use on dunes is not compatible with the natural processes, and whenever possible such usage should be eliminated entirely.

The habitats most severely affected by vehicles on barrier systems are salt marshes and sand flats. This intertidal environment harbors a variety of marine coastal organisms and supplies the primary productivity to the estuarine and nearshore marine food webs. The two main parts of the intertidal salt marshes are the high marsh (Spartina patens), flooded only by spring tides and the low marsh, dominated by Spartina alterniflora. The sand flats exposed at low tide serve as feeding grounds for shorebirds and are habitats for commercially important species such as the soft shell clam (Mya arenaria).

ORV impacts in the high salt marsh (dominated by Spartina patens) are substantial, but this zone is not extensively used for driving. Barren pathways through the high marsh can develop with minimal impact. Only two hundred passes kills all standing biomass. Where rapid repair of tracks across the high marsh is desired, management actions are needed, such as planting the site with appropriate species. In any case, all traffic should be restricted from the high marsh.

One of the most seriously affected regions in the intertidal environment is the upper sand flats. Although some flats are natural, the extensive barren sand flats along the bayshore of some islands are definitely maintained by ORV traffic. Once protected by enclosure, the sand flats are quickly invaded by low marsh species, especially glasswort (Salicornia), with colonization by salt marsh

76

cordgrass (Spartina alterniflora) requiring more time.

ORV traffic on the naturally open flats has also affected the survival of marine infauna, including worms, clams, and other mollusks. At Hatches Harbor, Cape Cod, there were marked reductions of marine animals in driven zones vs. non-driven sections. This implies that "normal" ORV activity does deplete population numbers and might be sufficient to eliminate these species in impacted areas.

Experimental tests were made on the survival of the soft shell clam (Mya arenaria) under relatively low levels of vehicle impact. The soft shell clam has historically been an important economic resource on Cape Cod, but this species has undergone a dramatic decline in recent years. A 20-day period of impacting clams 50 times per day resulted in total decimation of experimental animals and established the fact that clam populations can easily be depleted by vehicular traffic. Clams were killed directly by crushing of their relatively soft shells as well as by modification of their environment. Vehicles compacted the substrate into a pavement-like (macadam) surface, interfering with normal exchange of sea water and air in the sediments and creating anaerobic conditions. It also prevented clams from extending their siphons to the surface to obtain food and water at high tide, which eventually results in death to other filter-feeding organisms as well.

ORV activity across intertidal flats may have adverse effects not only at the species level, but at the systems level as well. This impact can result in the loss of important species and affect food-web complexity. Continued ORV disturbance can create biologically unproductive and aesthetically unappealing, barren areas. This intertidal environment cannot tolerate even light use by vehicles; it is imperative that all ORV traffic be prohibited.

Although the low salt marsh of Spartina alterniflora is rarely impacted, destruction by vehicles can be severe and long lasting. Less than 100 passes of a Jeep were possible in the experimental impacts because compaction of the peat created an impassable quagmire. Only one pass of a vehicle is sufficient to create ruts in the marsh peat that can persist for decades. These undrained depressions or pannes accumulate and retain salt water during each high tide. As evaporation proceeds, the salt content increases and reaches levels that preclude reinvasion by marsh plants. Artificial pannes also provide habitat for salt marsh mosquito larvae.

The best management approach is to close all salt marsh and tidal flat habitats to vehicle use. This ecological system is much too sensitive for such recreational purposes; it has no carrying capacity for vehicles. ORVs are a major stress to this environment, detrimental in all aspects thus far investigated. Where necessary, provision should be made for bypassing the marshes and flats by developing a series of carefully located upland trails. Once closed, the salt marsh and tidal flat system will begin to recover, but it must be patrolled and regulations enforced. Only a few illegal passes through protected areas will substantially set back recovery of vegetation. Interpretation programs should be instituted to educate the public on the need for protecting the intertidal environment and the damaging effects that vehicles have in such habitats.

Development Potential

Barrier Construction

Shoreline Engineering

Barrier island morphology is very changeable; beaches erode and accrete, dunes shift positions, washover fans are periodically active, and inlets open, migrate, and close. Development practices should conform to this inherent barrier instability and unpredictability. Ironically, development has been allowed to proceed on some of the most hazardous zones--washover fans and old inlet sites. These areas can be identified on historical aerial photographs, but developers and some licensing agencies have made little use of this scientific information in the planning process. The result has been the construction of private homes and public roads in highly vulnerable areas susceptible to flood damage, sand burial, or complete truncation by inlets.

Barrier Construction

In spite of inherent hazards, there has been a boom in barrier island construction during the past few decades. For instance, construction on pristine barriers has proceeded rapidly along the Florida Gulf coast. In addition, major capital investments have been made in revitalizing already urbanized barrier islands, such as those in New Jersey (Figure 76).

A prime example of this rapid urbanization is the construction of high-rise condominiums at Ocean City, Maryland. The intent of the developers was to build the "Miami Beach of the North" through the construction of a string of hotels and condominiums along the shoreline. These high-rise structures at Ocean City were built within a few hundred feet of an eroding shoreline. In the construction process, the dunes were customarily leveled in order to allow building as close to the shoreline as possible and to provide an ocean view for the lower floors.

Dunes are major storage areas for beach sand and play an important role in absorbing storm waves. Without this natural defense and buffer zone, the backbarrier areas become susceptible to high energy conditions during coastal storms. When stable features such as buildings and roadways are built on dynamic barrier surfaces in highly vulnerable positions, heavy damage can result from direct wave attack, overwash and flooding. Clearly, the leveling of barrier dunes increases these coastal hazards.

Land-use regulations and building codes should be used to protect barrier dunes and prohibit unwise development. Such positive action could prevent unnecessary loss of life and property during hurricanes and save millions of dollars in emergency costs and disaster relief. Setback lines that establish a minimum distance from the shoreline for development should be used as one such measure. Building setback distances can be determined from an analysis of the long-term rate of beach erosion.

More than 20 federal agencies administer programs that affect building on barrier islands. Some agency policies actively encourage and others even subsidize development on islands through programs of grants, permits, insurance, and disaster relief. These federal programs effectively reduce the financial risk to developers and inhabitants of barrier islands by transferring significant portions of the costs to the general taxpayers. Until recently a distinction was not made between barrier island and mainland projects in the management of these programs. In fact, without many of these federal incentives, much of the barrier development would not be possible. For instance, grants from EPA help to build sewage facilities and permits by the Coast Guard to build bridges facilitate such growth. More importantly, the Federal flood insurance program provides insurance and other assistance to allow for permanent human occupation in very hazardous areas. Similar insurance is not obtainable through the private sector due to the high risks involved.

Favorable government programs and absence of effective land-use regulations have enabled the buildup of private buildings and public utilities on dynamic barrier islands (Figure 77). As the

76. Legalized gambling has turned Atlantic City, New Jersey, from a waterfront slum into a showplace and mecca for sporting enthusiasts.

barrier retreats, these stable structures face the impact of the high energy swash/surf zone (Figure 78). Thus, there is a sharp contrast between man's static features and the barrier's dynamic nature, a contrast that becomes intensified through time. Extreme damage occurs during storms, when the stability of shorefront buildings is jeopardized by beach and dune erosion and exposure of building supports (Figure 79).

77. Miami Beach is a highly urbanized barrier, shown shortly after the beach fill project in 1980.

The folly of building one's house on shifting sands was even recognized by Biblical writers (Matthew 7:24-27). Each year another house topples into the crashing surf at Plum Island, Massachusetts (Figure 80). It is fortunate that these buildings are single family homes rather than multistory condominiums; otherwise, the cost and loss would be greatly amplified. Once a beach has eroded back to the very foundations of a house, it takes only the punch of the annual winter northeasters to deliver it to the storm waves below.

There have been similar losses of property and buildings along the U.S. East and Gulf coasts as barriers attempt to move landward, which is reflected as seaside beach erosion (Figure 81). For instance, continued erosion caused the Cape Henlopen (Delaware) Lighthouse to topple and fall into the sea in 1926 when its foundation was finally undermined.

Another example of human conflict with the sea is the attempt by the National Park Service to save the Cape Hatteras Lighthouse and adjacent Buxton motels by beach stabilization and other protective measures. Various engineering solutions were attempted, including groins, piling sand bags along the beach as a sea wall, beach nourishment and dune construction, but with little success. Over twenty million dollars was spent in these futile efforts, yet today the lighthouse is less than a hundred feet from the water's edge. In retrospect, it may have been less expensive to purchase the Buxton motels and move the Lighthouse than to attempt to stabilize the shoreline. Although it can be argued that some time has been bought at Cape Hatteras, the associated costs have been extremely high.

78. A local developer at Ocean City, Maryland, proved that restrictions on development were not binding by building his house on the active beach face, in spite of all the regulations to the contrary.

79. The large condominiums at Ocean City, Maryland. (built in the 1970s) are already susceptible to storm damage. Note that the pilings are exposed and the tie rods and concrete supports have already been broken by wave attack.

80. A large house on Plum Island, Massachusetts, plummets into the sea during a winter storm.

There is really no erosion problem until people build on the shore. After this commitment has been made, there is a tendency to go to great lengths to protect this initial investment. Buildings located in hazardous areas necessitate protective measures, which are usually expensive to construct and maintain. Such projects have often proceeded without a clear understanding of the long-term impacts or costs. Although protective devices can be successful locally over the short term, large expenditures of money are usually necessary on a continuing basis. Shoreline engineering techniques, their design and usefulness, are described in the final section.

81. The New England Blizzard of February 6-7, 1978 obliterated the Coast Guard Beach facility on Nauset Spit in Eastham, Cape Cod, Massachusetts.

There are essentially two approaches to beach protection and shoreline stabilization: rigid structures, such as jetties, and nonrigid techniques, such as beach nourishment. The rigid devices fall into two basic categories: structures to trap longshore transport of sand (e.g., groins and jetties) and structures to prevent the erosion of the shoreline (principally with seawalls). Groins, seawalls, and other engineering devices are designed to impede waves and currents and hence inhibit sand transport. Due to the high

82. Groins can be constructed of stone, steel sheetpile, timber or other materials. This groin along the southern New Jersey coast is formed with large, quarried rocks.

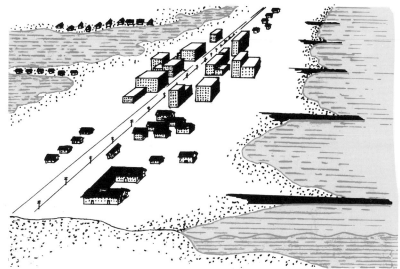

83. The desired effects of a groin field are illustrated.

cost of emplacement, these rigid structures are used only in localized areas to protect urbanized development in hazardous locations.

Groins are shore protection structures which extend from the beach backshore into the surf zone, perpendicular to the shoreline (Figure 82). A groin is intended to build up an eroded beach by trapping littoral drift, or to retard the erosion of a stretch of beach which has been artificially widened. A groin or jetty interrupts the flow of longshore sediment transport, causing sand to be deposited against the structure's updrift side. As the longshore current is re-established downdrift of the littoral barrier, the quantity of sand being transported is less than the "saturated" value, resulting in erosion downdrift of the structure (Figure 82).

85

The apparent solution to this problem is to build a series of groins to protect a long section of shoreline (Figure 83), but there are various problems associated with their construction. The dimensions and spacing between groins are critical; the result can be a failure of the groin field to fill or improper re-establishment of the longshore current pattern. In the latter case, interruption of the littoral drift can result in some of the sediment being directed offshore as it passes around the outer ends of the groins. Consequently, groins can decrease the amount of sand in the littoral drift system that was available to nourish the beach. In addition, construction of groins does not solve the beach erosion problem but merely

shifts it downdrift. These devices that trap sand drifting along the coast are merely "robbing Peter to pay Paul," since no new sand is created. While groins have been in use for some time, their functional design is still a matter of considerable discussion. Some groins have satisfied their intended purpose, but most have been either ineffective or have had detrimental effects.

Jetties are essentially one or two groins built at the sides of an inlet to protect and maintain navigable inlets. Their purpose is to stabilize an inlet by catching the longshore transport of sand that would otherwise fill it in or cause it to shift position. Sand moving by the

84. Jetties at Ocean City, Maryland, have intercepted a major portion of the littoral drift. The result has been the accretion of a large triangular beach section on the updrift side, necessitating the lengthening of the fishing pier. More seriously, the northern end of Assateague Island has undergone severe erosion, averaging 30-40 feet per year since inlet stabilization in 1935. Due to sand starvation, Assateague has been pushed landward by a distance exceeding the barrier's width. Assateague and Fenwick Islands were connected as a relatively straight shoreline before emplacement of the jetties.

longshore currents is trapped on the updrift side of the jetty, resulting in beach accretion. Beaches downdrift of the stabilized inlet become sand-starved and consequently erode (Figure 84). Sand bypassing, through continuous dredging of sediment from the accreting side for discharge on the eroding downdrift side, can be employed to maintain the natural longshore flow (of littoral drift). This procedure is expensive, and it represents a continual, long-term commitment of funds and resources.

Seawalls, bulkheads, and revetments are rigid structures built parallel to the shoreline to serve as barriers to wave attack and storm-surge flooding. These artificial structures essentially replace or reinforce the dunes that serve as the natural barriers to flood water. Hence, seawalls may be quite effective in protecting backbarrier areas, but often at the expense of a recreational beach (Figure 85).

Seawalls are massive, inflexible structures, which prevent the natural exchange of sand between the dune and beach during storms; this material is needed to build up the offshore profile. Also, a significant portion of the wave energy can be reflected off the seawall face and downward, increasing the strength of the longshore current and accelerating the rate of beach erosion.

With an eroding shoreline and a static seawall, the two lines will eventually converge, resulting in the complete loss of a beach. Without beach nourishment or some other means of toe protection, the seawall will collapse, being undermined during a severe storm (Figure 86). The resulting loss of life and property could be catastrophic.

Large amounts of money have been spent on

85. The seawall at Galveston Island, Texas, was built to protect the city from hurricane surges. The beach has been subsequently lost.

coastal engineering structures, but many are ineffective and some have aggravated existing problems. The best solution is to employ more natural approaches, such as dune building and beach nourishment. These nonrigid techniques do not interfere greatly with natural processes.

One of the simplest ways of providing protection to backbarrier areas is the construction of barrier dunes. Sand fencing (Figure 87) or planting beach grass (Figure 88) are the primary methods

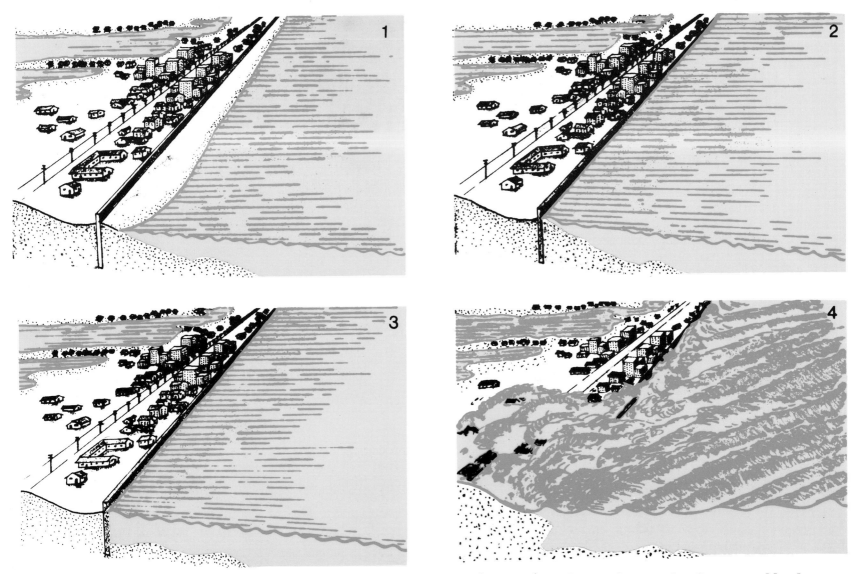

86. This sequence demonstrates the inevitable problems associated with the emplacement of a seawall along an eroding shoreline. Without artificial sand nourishment, the beach will be eventually lost, and seawall failure during a storm can result in catastrophic loss of life and property.

87. Sand fencing can be used to quickly build dunes as shown at Cape Hatteras, North Carolina. With the
rapid rate of shoreline erosion and frequent, high intensity storm characteristics of the Cape, the
newly-formed dune will probably have a short life span.

used to encourage dune development. The most
effective technique is to use snow fencing to
collect windblown sand. Once the fences are filled
to capacity, beach plants can be placed on the new,
artificially-induced dune; a spring-time planting is
preferable in most regions.

Barrier dunes are an important and natural
part of most migrating barrier island systems.
The importance of dunes as a means of natural beach
protection has been recognized, and dunes should
be restored where destroyed during development or
disturbed by recreational impacts.

Artificially-induced dunes that are high and
unbroken form an effective barrier to storm waves,
reducing the amount of salt spray and preventing
overwash. This can result in vegetational changes
through ecologic succession. Woody species,
primarily the shrub community, are able to displace

the grasses as they spread seaward. At Cape
Hatteras, North Carolina, impenetrable thickets
over 15 feet high have formed in the lee of the
protective dune. When the dunes are finally
breached during a major hurricane, these woody
species are killed, and grasses once again invade
and colonize the newly deposited sand.

The geological implications of barrier dune
stabilization have also been debated. Some
researchers have argued that dunes interfere with
the energy dissipation process and thus accelerate
the rate of beach erosion. During extreme events
a high dune becomes vertically scarped; this
impenetrable barrier to storm waves forces the
runoff seaward and may actually reflect the waves.
However, to draw an analogy between seawalls and
eroding dunes does not take into account the distinction between static and dynamic behavior.
Even when a dune is stabilized by vegetation, it is

88. American beach grass plants (<u>Ammophila</u>) are sprigged in April at North Beach, Massachusetts. This work was undertaken, in part, to offset the devegetation and dune disturbance due to vehicular impacts.

still essentially a part of the dynamic system and becomes a sand stockpile for storm events.

Although man-made dunes can halt barrier migration in the short term, barrier dunes will eventually be breached by overwashes and inlets during a severe storm along an eroding shoreline. Dunes, therefore, have no long-term adverse effects on barrier island dynamics. Stabilized dunes have, however, encouraged development in highly hazardous areas by offering a false sense of security to

backbarrier environments.

Beach nourishment is probably the most effective way to deal with beach erosion problems. In essence, sand is supplied to the beach at the same rate that it is naturally being lost alongshore or offshore. The problem with beach nourishment is locating nearby sources of unpolluted sand of the correct size. In the past, sediments were dredged from the adjacent bay and pumped onto the beach. This procedure resulted in environmental damage to the estuarine ecosystem, and much of the material was too fine to remain on the active beach face. As silts and clays were rapidly flushed offshore by the breaking waves and currents, the nourished beach eroded with little net gain. The size and composition of beach fill should closely match the native sand or be slightly coarser grained.

Potential sources for beach nourishment are ebb-tidal deltas and offshore relict sediments on the inner continental shelf, seaward of the nearshore sand-sharing system. With the introduction of enough new sand, beach erosion can be held in check and the barrier essentially frozen in place. The cost associated with such ambitious projects often exceeds a million dollars per mile of shoreline. The recently completed beach nourishment program at Miami Beach cost over sixty million dollars for a ten mile section of beach (Figure 89). This was the most extensive and expensive project undertaken anywhere in the world with the simple goal of placing sand on a beach. The great advantage of beach nourishment is that the barrier island ecosystems are largely unmanipulated; the island responds as if it were naturally receiving a large input of new sand.

In summary, attempts to stabilize transgres-

89. The Miami Beach nourishment project where sand pumped from offshore resulted in a 300 foot wide beach (Corps of Engineers).

sive barrier islands will ultimately fail as sea level continues to rise. While engineering structures may be successful in localized areas, long-term problems are ultimately created, and substantial maintenance costs are incurred with this approach.

Barrier islands will continue to change shape and migrate landward; the time frame is island-specific, ranging from decades to millenia. The eventual loss of buildings located on the most dynamic barriers should be expected and accepted. The strategy should be to avoid construction at vulnerable locations; this would translate to little or no development potential for some islands. Only low-density and low-cost development should be allowed on migrating barrier islands. This type of building policy would never permit the high levels of human occupation on barrier islands that are presently allowed.

Attempts to stabilize barriers are expensive and sometimes ineffective. Groins, seawalls, and other rigid structures should only be used to protect a highly urbanized area and thus avert substantial human and economic loss during a catastrophic storm. In such cases, economic analyses should be made to determine whether the value of the investments warrant the high and continuing cost. As a corollary to the above, the construction of new, expensive buildings, such as high-rise condominiums, on unstable barrier islands should be avoided. These developments will eventually require protection with massive outlays of tax dollars for engineering structures and disaster relief following future major storms.

Bibliography

Bruun, P. 1962. Sea-Level Rise as a Cause of Shore Erosion: Proceedings of American Society of Civil Engineers, Journal of Waterways and Harbors Division: V. 88, p. 117-130.

Fisher, J. 1968. Barrier Island Formation: Discussion. Geological Society of America Bulletin, V. 79, p. 1421-1426.

Hayes, M. 1979. Barrier Island Morphology as a Function of Tidal and Wave Regime, in Barrier Island, S. Leatherman (ed.), Academic Press, Inc., New York, p. 1-28.

Hicks, S. 1972. On the Classification and Trends of Long Period Sea Level Series, Shore and Beach, V. 40, p. 20-23.

Hoyt, J. 1967. Barrier Island Formation. Geological Society of America Bulletin, V. 78, p. 1125-1136.

Leatherman, S.P., ed. 1979. Barrier Islands, Academic Press, Inc., New York, N.Y., 325 pp.

Leatherman, S. 1979. Barrier Dune Systems: A Reassessment. Sedimentary Geology, V. 24, p. 1-16.

Leatherman, S. and P. Godfrey. 1979. The Impact of Off-Road Vehicles on Coastal Ecosystems in Cape Cod National Seashore: An Overview. University of Massachusetts-National Park Service Research Unit. Report No. 34, 34 p.

Leatherman, S. 1981. Overwash Processes, Benchmark Papers in Geology, Hutchinson and Ross, Inc., Stroudsburg, Pa., 376 p.

Leatherman, S., T. Rice, and V. Goldsmith. 1982. Virginia Barrier Island Configuration: A Reappraisal. Science, V. 215, p. 285-287.

Leatherman, S.P. 1988. Cape Cod Field Trips: From Glaciers to Beaches, University of Maryland, College Park, MD, 132 pp.

Mathewson, C., J. Clary, and J. Stinson. 1975. Dynamic Physical Processes on a South Texas Barrier Island--Impact on Construction and Maintenance. IEEE Oceans 75, p. 327-330.

Milliman, J. and K. Emery. 1968. Sea levels During the Past 35,000 Years. Science, V. 162, p. 1121-1123.

Oertel, G.F. and S.P. Leatherman 1985. Barrier Islands, Elsevier, Amsterdam, 396 pp.

Redfield, A., 1972. Development of a New England Salt Marsh. Ecological Monographs, V. 42, p. 210-237.

Shepard, F. and H. Wanless. 1971. Our Changing Coastlines. McGraw-Hill Inc., New York, 577 p.

U.S. Army Corps of Engineers. 1974. Shore Protection Manual. Coastal Engineering Research Center, Vicksburg, Miss.